gateway science

revision guide

OCR Science for GCSE

Separate

Physics

Pauline Anning • Carol Tear

Series editor: Bob McDuell

Heinemann

Heinemann is an imprint of Pearson Education Limited,
a company incorporated in England Wales,
having its registered office at Edinburgh Gate, Harlow,
Essex, CM20 2JE. Registered company number: 872828

Heinemann is a registered trademark of Pearson Education Limited

© Harcourt Education Limited 2007

First published 2007

11 10
10 9 8 7 6 5 4

British Library Cataloguing in Publication Data is available from the British Library on request.

ISBN: 978 0 435675 50 9

Designed by Wooden Ark
Project managed, edited and typeset by Bookcraft Ltd (Alex Sharpe, Project Manager)

Pearson project team: David Cooke, Andrew Halcro-Johnston, Ross Laman, Sarah Ross, Ruth Simms, Iti Singh, Peter Stratton

Original illustrations © Harcourt Education Limited 2007

Illustrated by Bookcraft India Pvt Ltd (Gemma Raj), HL Studios

Printed in China (CTPS/04)

Cover photo © Getty Images

Every effort has been made to contact copyright holders of material reproduced in this book. Any omissions will be rectified in subsequent printings if notice is given to the publishers.

About this book

This OCR Gateway Physics revision guide will help you revise for the OCR Gateway Physics exams. One exam consists of modules P1, P2 and P3 and the other of P4, P5 and P6. The guide summarises what you have learnt and links directly to the OCR Physics specification for Higher tier.

This guide is broken down into the six physics modules: P1, P2, P3, P4, P5 and P6. Each module covers eight items (a–h), for example P1a–P1h. You will find some items are combined into one section, for example P1b & P1c.

Each section starts with a **learning outcome** which summarises the main points covered. This will help you to focus on what you need to revise in that section.

Key words are shown in bold and you will find them indexed at the back of the guide. **Equations** are highlighted to help you use and apply them.

The exam may ask you to consider ideas about 'How science works'. The **How science works** boxes will help you apply this thinking to your answers. Remember that you should be continually questioning how scientists collect data, use and interpret evidence.

Exam tips highlight common mistakes and give you advice about exam preparation so you can achieve better grades.

You will find lots of simple, full colour diagrams, including **spider diagrams**, to help with your revision and to make the content more digestible. Try drawing your own spider diagrams to help you remember key concepts.

We have given you **'Test yourself' questions** at the end of each section to help you to check that you have understood the content. Use the **answers** at the back of the guide to check whether you have got them all correct – if not, go back and revise that section again.

The revision guide is based on the new specification and the example **exam-style questions** on page 70 will give you valuable preparation for the exams.

Remember that these questions are for revision and homework. The exams will also contain some recall and one-mark questions. In your revision you should think beyond the basic ideas so that you have a better understanding for the exams.

The **answers** that follow the questions will allow you to check your progress and improve next time.

Good luck with your exams!

Contents

P1a Heating houses

After revising this item you should:

- understand the difference between heat and temperature, explain what happens when a substance is heated and calculate heat energies.

Temperature and heat

Temperature is a measure of how hot or cold an object is on a chosen scale. Temperature is measured in degrees Celsius (°C).

Heat is a measurement of energy on an absolute scale. Heat is measured in joules (J).

The temperature of different parts of an object can be shown using a **thermogram**. The hotter parts appear red, the colder parts appear blue.

Energy flow

Heat energy always flows from a hotter object to a cooler one. The hotter an object is the faster the rate at which it loses heat energy.

- An object that is hotter than its surroundings will lose heat energy and cool down.
- An object that is cooler than its surroundings will gain heat energy and warm up.

Exam tip

You can remember this by imagining hot and cold drinks sitting on a table.

- *A hot cup of coffee loses heat energy to the surroundings and cools down.*
- *A cold glass of lemonade gains heat energy from the surroundings and warms up.*

Specific heat capacity

The amount of energy needed to change the temperature of an object depends on:

- its mass
- the material it is made from
- the size of the temperature change.

Equal masses of different materials need different amounts of energy for the same temperature change.

The **specific heat capacity** of a material is:

- the energy needed to raise the temperature of 1 kg of the material by 1°C.

The units of specific heat capacity are joules per kilogram per degree Celsius (J/kg/°C).

The greater the specific heat capacity of a material the more energy it can hold.

The equation for this is:

$$\text{energy (J)} = \text{mass (kg)} \times \text{specific heat capacity} \times \text{temperature change (°C)} \\ \text{(J/kg/°C)}$$

Exam tip

You need to be able to use this equation and you may need to rearrange it in an exam question, for example:

$$specific\ heat\ capacity = \frac{energy}{(mass \times temperature\ change)}$$

Melting and boiling

Melting is changing from solid into liquid, boiling is changing from liquid into gas. These changes are called changes of **state** and energy is needed to make them happen.

Different materials melt and boil at different temperatures. While a material is melting or boiling there is no change in temperature because the energy being supplied is used to overcome the forces of attraction between particles in the solid or liquid, breaking the intermolecular bonds.

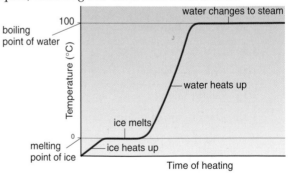

The graph shows what happens when ice is heated until it first becomes water, and then the water becomes steam. The horizontal parts of the graph show that:

- the temperature stays at 0°C while the ice melts
- and it stays at 100°C while the water changes to steam.

Specific latent heat

The **specific latent heat** of a material is:

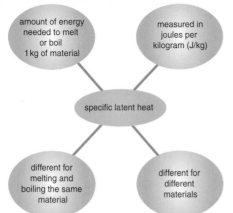

The equation for specific latent heat is:

energy (J) = mass (kg) × specific latent heat (J/kg)

Freezing

Freezing is changing from liquid into solid, such as from water to ice. When a material freezes it loses energy, but there is no change in temperature.

Test yourself

1 Calculate the energy required to raise the temperature of 3 kg of water from 10°C to 20°C. The specific heat capacity of water is 4200 J/kg/°C.

2 In an experiment a block of iron is heated to 125°C and left to cool to 25°C. As it cools it gives out 88 000 J of heat energy. The mass of the block is 2 kg. What is the specific heat capacity of iron?

3 Why does adding ice at 0°C cool your drink more than adding water at 0°C?

4 A student adds some ice to a drink. The ice all melts as 9900 J of energy is transferred to it from the drink. The specific latent heat of ice is 330 000 J/kg. Calculate the mass of ice the student added to the drink.

5 Why is a burn from steam at 100°C likely to be worse than a burn from water at 100°C?

P1b Keeping homes warm & P1c How insulation works

After revising these items you should:

● be able to compare the payback time of different types of insulation, explain what is meant by conduction, convection and radiation and how we can reduce heat loss by these processes.

Saving money

Reducing the heat energy losses from a house saves the householder money on fuel bills. Any energy-saving features added by the householder will cost money to install. A way of working out the cost-effectiveness of these features is called the **payback time**.

$$\text{payback time (years)} = \frac{\text{installation cost (£)}}{\text{fuel saving (£ per year)}}$$

Efficiency

The **efficiency** of a system tells you how much of the energy that goes into that system is usefully transferred. The rest of the energy is wasted.

You can calculate efficiency using the equation:

$$\text{efficiency} = \frac{\textbf{useful energy output}}{\textbf{total energy input}}$$

Transfer of heat energy

Heat energy is transferred by:

• **conduction**

• **convection**

• **radiation**

An energy efficient home reduces the transfer of energy by each of these processes. This means that less energy is wasted and the householder saves money.

Conduction

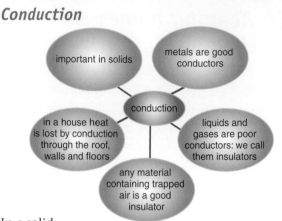

In a solid:

- the particles are held together by strong forces, but vibrate continuously about fixed positions
- heating one end of a solid gives the particles more **kinetic energy** so they vibrate more.

This causes neighbouring particles to vibrate more, and in this way kinetic energy is passed between the particles.

In liquids and gases:

- the forces between particles are weaker than in solids
- the particles are able to move around and energy does not easily pass from particle to particle as in solids.

Air is a poor conductor so materials that contain air, such as glass fibre, are good insulators.

Convection

When a gas is heated it expands, becomes less dense and rises. This change of density causes fluid flow as the rising warm gas is replaced by falling colder gas, which has a higher density.

In this way a convection current is set up that transfers heat through the gas. Convection also takes place in liquids, for the same reason.

Exam tip

You must be able to explain convection currents in terms of different densities. Warm air rises because it has a lower density; cold air sinks because it has a higher density. It is not enough to say simply 'hot air rises' and 'cold air falls'.

Cavity walls reduce energy loss by conduction, but as the air inside them flows, heat is lost by convection instead. We can reduce this heat loss by adding cavity wall insulation, which traps the air in pockets, preventing convection.

Radiation

All objects lose heat energy through waves called **infrared** radiation. This radiation does not need a medium to travel through and is the way that heat energy from the Sun reaches us through space.

Light, shiny surfaces reflect infrared radiation. A layer of shiny foil placed on a wall behind a heater reflects infrared radiation back into the room. This reduces energy loss through the wall. Painting the outside walls of a house white also reduces energy loss by radiation as light, shiny surfaces are poor emitters of radiation.

Exam tip

In explaining how a particular method of reducing heat loss works, make sure you explain which type(s) of heat loss it reduces.

Test yourself

1 Why does a stone floor feel colder to your feet than a carpet?

2 Cavity wall insulation costs £800 to install and saves £200 per year on fuel. A porch costs £700 to install and saves £150 per year. Which has the shorter payback time?

3 Why are hot water tanks often covered with a jacket made from glass fibre?

4 For every 100 J of energy supplied to a gas central heating system 92 J are usefully transferred as heat. Calculate the efficiency of the system.

5 An electric fan heater has an efficiency of 0.96.

   (a) Calculate the useful heat energy output produced by the heater when 50 J of electrical energy are input.

   (b) Suggest what happens to the energy that is not usefully transferred as heat in the fan heater.

6 Explain why two walls with an air-filled cavity between them are more effective at reducing heat loss than a single wall.

7 Explain why filling the cavity between two walls with foam or polystyrene beads is more effective at reducing heat loss than an air-filled cavity.

8 Explain why wearing white clothes in a hot country will keep you cooler than wearing black clothes.

P1d Cooking with waves & P1e Infrared signals

After revising these items you should:

- be able to explain some applications of infrared radiation and microwaves and the advantages of using digital signals.

Cooking with infrared

Infrared radiation is the heat source in toasters, cookers and grills. The infrared radiation is absorbed by all particles on the surface of the food, increasing their kinetic energy, and this increases the temperature of the food. The energy is transferred to the centre of the food by conduction or convection.

Infrared radiation is reflected by shiny surfaces such as tin foil.

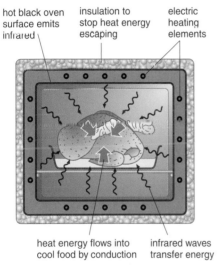

hot black oven surface emits infrared

insulation to stop heat energy escaping

electric heating elements

heat energy flows into cool food by conduction

infrared waves transfer energy

Cooking with microwaves

Microwaves can also be used for cooking:

- The microwaves produced in a microwave oven penetrate about 1 cm into the food. They are absorbed by water molecules in the outside layers of the food, increasing their kinetic energy and raising the temperature of the food.

- The energy is transferred to the centre of the food from the outside by conduction or convection.

- Microwaves pass through glass and plastic but are reflected by metal, so most of the microwaves stay inside the oven.

The water in body tissue will absorb microwaves and the heat released can cause burns.

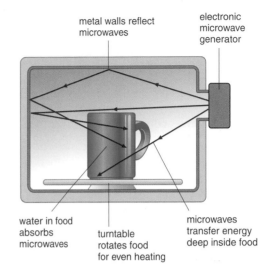

metal walls reflect microwaves

electronic microwave generator

water in food absorbs microwaves

turntable rotates food for even heating

microwaves transfer energy deep inside food

Energy in waves

Like infrared radiation and visible light, microwaves are part of the electromagnetic spectrum. Different radiations in this spectrum have different properties and uses but they all travel as waves, carrying energy through empty space.

The amount of energy carried by an electromagnetic wave depends on its **frequency**. The higher the frequency, the greater the energy and the more dangerous the radiation. Visible light has a higher frequency than infrared radiation, which has a higher frequency than microwaves.

Microwaves and mobile phones

Mobile phones use microwave signals which are transmitted first between the mobile phone and a mobile phone mast, and then between masts.

The microwaves can carry information over long distances provided that they are in 'line of sight'. This is because microwaves cannot bend round corners or over mountains. Places that are not in line of sight with a mast will get a poor signal.

Over long distances the signal may become weakened by interference or **diffraction**, so the transmitters are placed fairly close together and high up away from obstacles.

As the microwaves from your mobile phone pass through your brain they heat it up slightly. Some people are concerned that the use of mobile phones may cause brain tumours, and they may be a particular danger to young children.

Mobile phone masts emit much more radiation than a mobile phone. Many people are concerned about masts placed in their communities.

So far it has not been proved that the masts are harmful. However, this may change as further research is carried out.

Analogue and digital signals

Two types of signal are used to transmit data, **analogue** and **digital**.

- Analogue signals have a continuously variable value.
- Digital signals are either on (1) or off (0).

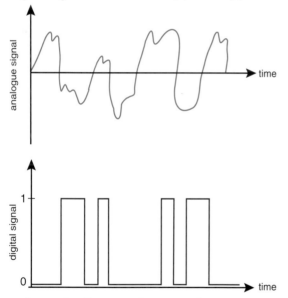

Digital signals allow much more information to be transmitted because many signals can be interleaved on the same data line without interfering with each other. This is called **multiplexing**.

All signals weaken as they travel and need to be amplified. When an analogue signal is amplified any noise (unwanted signals) is also amplified and this causes distortion. When a digital signal is amplified any noise is removed beforehand and is not amplified.

Make sure you can sketch graphs like the ones shown to illustrate both analogue and digital signals.

Total internal reflection

A ray of light travelling in a transparent material, such a water, glass or perspex, is **refracted** (changes direction) when it reaches a boundary. The ray only passes out of the material if the angle of incidence is less than the **critical angle**.

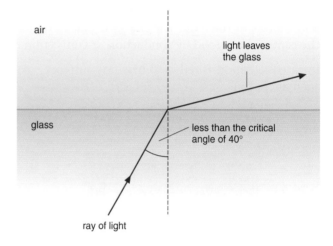

If the angle of incidence is the same as the critical angle the light travels along the surface. If the angle of incidence is greater than the critical angle **total internal reflection** takes place.

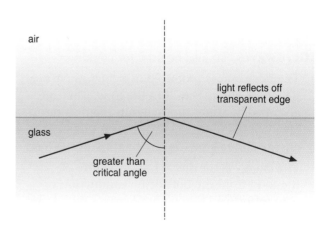

Optical fibres

Infrared or visible light signals are used to transmit data very rapidly along **optical fibres**.

Here are some properties of optical fibres:

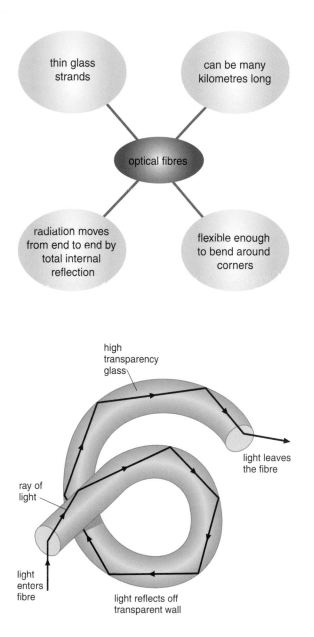

- thin glass strands
- can be many kilometres long
- optical fibres
- radiation moves from end to end by total internal reflection
- flexible enough to bend around corners

high transparency glass

light leaves the fibre

ray of light

light enters fibre

light reflects off transparent wall

Test yourself

1 Why are glass and plastic, but not metal dishes, used when cooking food in a microwave oven?

2 Explain the difference between analogue and digital signals.

3 The critical angle for a piece of glass is 42°. A ray of light inside the glass hits the side at an angle of incidence of 38°. What happens to the ray?

4 Name two types of electromagnetic waves used to carry signals along optical fibres.

5 Why is the transmission of light signals along optical fibres a very fast way to transmit data?

P1f Wireless signals

After revising this item you should:

- be able to describe some uses of wireless technology, explain how electromagnetic waves are reflected, refracted and diffracted and how this affects communication.

Uses of wireless technology

The uses of **wireless technology** include:

- radio
- mobile phones
- connecting laptop computers to the Internet.

Refraction

Electromagnetic waves change direction when they cross the boundary from one material into another. This is called refraction.

The change in direction occurs because the waves change speed as they cross the boundary. The speed of the wave depends on the material it is passing through.

Radio waves are refracted as they pass through layers of air of different densities in the Earth's atmosphere. This allows them to bend around the curve of the Earth's surface.

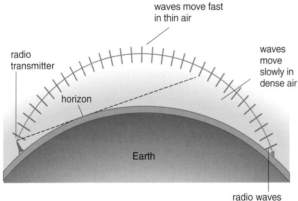

waves move fast in thin air

waves move slowly in dense air

radio transmitter

horizon

Earth

radio waves arrive over the horizon

Exam tip

Remember that when a wave moves from one material into another its speed and wavelength change, but its frequency stays the same.

Radio transmissions

Radio stations broadcast their signals from transmitter masts to radio stations in our homes. If you are a long distance from the mast the signal you receive will be weak and you will not be able to hear the radio programme clearly. The mast has to be positioned above your horizon to provide you with a good signal.

The transmitter mast emits lots of different frequencies of radio waves at once. Each radio station is allocated its own set of **transmission frequencies**, so you tune your radio to a particular frequency to receive a particular station. This reduces interference – picking up unwanted signals from other stations.

Long distance radio transmissions

Radio waves used for long distance transmissions can be reflected off a charged layer in the upper atmosphere called the **ionosphere**.

We can also achieve long distance transmissions using microwaves (the shortest of the radio waves). These:

* travel in straight lines

* pass through the Earth's atmosphere

* are received by a **satellite** in a geostationary **orbit**

* are retransmitted to another receiver on the Earth.

Diffraction

Diffraction is the spreading out of waves when they pass through a gap or around an obstacle. The effect is most noticeable when the size of the gap or obstacle is similar to the wavelength of the wave.

The dish on a transmitter collects the waves and sends them into space.

* If the diameter of the dish is similar to the wavelength of the waves diffraction occurs, the waves spread as they travel and some of the signal is lost.

* If the diameter of the dish is much larger than the wavelength of the waves the signal does not spread out, so a stronger signal is produced.

Exam tip

Make sure that you can explain the difference between reflection, refraction and diffraction.

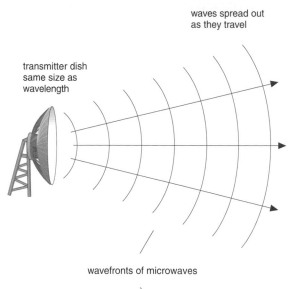

waves spread out
as they travel

transmitter dish
same size as
wavelength

wavefronts of microwaves

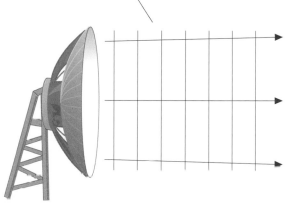

dish larger than
wave length

waves stay in
a beam as they travel

Digital radio

This table compares the properties of analogue and digital radio:

Analogue	Digital
A separate set of frequencies. This limits the number of stations that can operate in each area.	Uses digital coding. This results in better reception with less noise or interference.
In some places reflected and direct signals may interfere, giving a poor quality signal.	Each station has the same channel all over the country, so there is no need to retune.
Each station has a different channel in different areas, so if you are travelling you have to retune to keep a clear signal.	Many different stations can broadcast in each area.

Test yourself

1 Why do waves refract as they cross the boundaries between materials?

2 Why might security be a problem for wireless networks?

3 Why are communications satellites placed in geostationary orbits?

4 Suggest two advantages of digital signals compared with analogue.

5 When are diffraction effects most noticeable?

P1g Light

After revising this item you should:

● be able to identify the different parts of a transverse wave, use the wave equation to make calculations and explain some ways in which light is used for communications.

Electromagnetic waves

Electromagnetic waves are **transverse waves**.

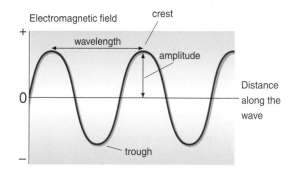

A transverse wave consists of **crests** and **troughs**.

● The **amplitude** of a transverse wave is the height of a crest.

● The **wavelength** is the distance from one crest to the next.

● The unit of wavelength is metres (m).

● The frequency is the number of waves per second.

● The unit of frequency is hertz (Hz).

9

Exam tip

Make sure that you can sketch a diagram to illustrate the difference parts of a transverse wave.

Wave equation

The speed, wavelength and frequency of a wave are related by the equation

wave speed (m/s) = frequency (Hz) × wavelength (m)

All electromagnetic waves travel at the same high speed through the vacuum of space. This speed is sometimes called the 'speed of light' and is 300 000 000 m/s.

Exam tip

Remember that as the frequency of an electromagnetic wave decreases its wavelength increases as the speed stays the same.

Morse code

Historical communications systems used light or electrical signals to carry messages as fast as the light or electrical signal could travel. This required the use of codes.

One well-known code is the **Morse code**, which uses dots and dashes to represent letters. It was first used to send messages through wires by pulsing the current in them on and off. It can also be used with a signal lamp or torch that is switched on and off to produce pulses of light.

Pulses of light are now used in many communications systems to transfer information.

Light, radio and electrical signals

These signals can all be used as means of communication:

- Light in optical fibres.
- Radio waves.
- Electrical pulses in wires.

They all carry information at the same speed, literally the 'speed of light'.

However, the amount of information they can carry varies: it depends on the frequency of the wave. Since light has a much higher frequency than radio waves it can carry much more information per second.

Another advantage of light is that it is not affected by magnetic and electric fields, but radio and electrical signals are.

The advantage of radio signals is that they are sent through the air without needing a connection, but light signals need to be sent down optical fibres and electrical signals require connecting wires.

Lasers

A **laser** produces an intense beam of light in which all of the waves are:

- the same frequency
- in phase with each other.

Lasers are used to read the information stored on a compact disc (CD). The information is stored as a digital code consisting of a series of pits in the surface of a plastic disc. Laser light reflects from the shiny surface (which contains digital information) of the disc onto a detector. This is read as a 1. Each time a pit passes under the laser the amount of light reflected decreases and this is read as a 0.

Lasers are also used:

- to send light down optical fibres
- to read bar codes on products in supermarkets.

Test yourself

1 What is meant by the frequency of a wave?

2 What is the speed of a wave with a frequency of 19 Hz and a wavelength of 10 mm? Include an appropriate unit with your answer.

3 A wave has a speed of 96 m/s and a wavelength of 8 cm. Calculate the frequency of the wave.

4 Suggest one advantage of using wires instead of light to send messages in Morse code.

5 Why can light signals carry more information than radio signals?

P1h Stable Earth

After revising this item you should:

- be able to explain some effects of ultraviolet radiation on the skin, describe how seismic waves can be used to provide evidence for the structure of the Earth and explain some reasons for climate change.

Earthquakes

The energy released by an **earthquake** travels through the Earth as seismic shock waves. These waves can cause enormous damage. They can be detected and measured by devices called seismometers.

There are two types of seismic waves: **P-waves** and **S-waves**.

P-waves	S-waves
longitudinal waves travel faster than S-waves travel through solids and liquids	transverse waves travel slower than P-waves only travel through solids

P-waves can travel through solid rock and liquid rock, so they can travel through all layers of the Earth. S-waves cannot travel through the liquid outer core.

By comparing the time difference between P-waves and S-waves arriving at seismic measuring stations located at different points on the Earth's surface, scientists have been able to construct a theory of the structure of the Earth.

Exam tip

*Remember that **S**-waves travel **s**lower than P-waves. After an earthquake, P-waves arrive at a seismic measuring station first.*

Ultraviolet radiation

Ultraviolet radiation is part of the electromagnetic spectrum. The Earth receives ultraviolet radiation from the Sun. Ultraviolet radiation has a higher frequency than visible light and carries more energy.

Darker skins are at less risk of damage from ultraviolet radiation because they absorb more of the radiation in the top layers, so less reaches the live skin cells below the surface.

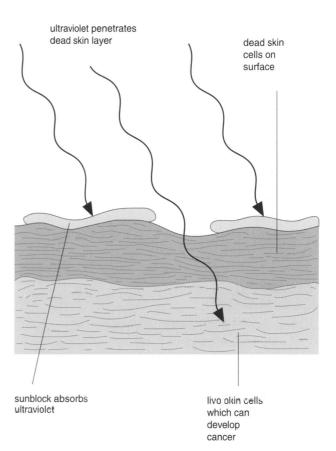

ultraviolet penetrates dead skin layer

dead skin cells on surface

sunblock absorbs ultraviolet

live skin cells which can develop cancer

Sun blocks absorb ultraviolet radiation and so protect the skin. The **sun protection factor**, SPF, indicates how long you can expect to stay in the sun without burning. For example an SPF of 10 indicates you can stay in the sun without burning for 10 times longer than without protection.

Ozone layer

The **ozone** layer, high up in the Earth's atmosphere, absorbs much of the ultraviolet radiation from the Sun, stopping it reaching the Earth.

There is evidence that artificial chemicals called CFCs are destroying this layer. If this is the case more ultraviolet radiation will reach the surface of the Earth. This is likely to increase the incidence of skin cancer.

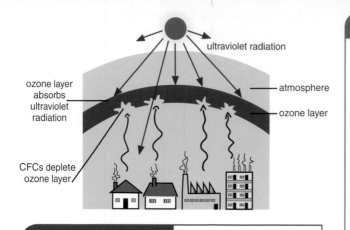

ozone layer absorbs ultraviolet radiation

CFCs deplete ozone layer

ultraviolet radiation

atmosphere

ozone layer

How science works

Scientists have shown strong links between exposure to ultraviolet radiation and skin cancer. Effective sun protection products have been developed, yet still many people continue to sunbathe without protecting their skin.

Exam tip

Remember that the higher the frequency of electromagnetic radiation the more energy it carries and the more dangerous it is.

Climate change

The Earth absorbs infrared and light radiation from the Sun, heating it. The Earth emits infrared radiation into space, cooling it.

Climate changes can come about as a result of both natural events and human activity:

- Dust from volcanoes reflects electromagnetic radiation from the Sun, which causes cooling.
- Dust from factories reflects electromagnetic radiation from cities back down to Earth, causing warming.
- The increased burning of fossil fuels to provide energy puts carbon dioxide into the atmosphere. This stops infrared radiation escaping from the Earth and causes warming.
- Burning forests also increases the amount of carbon dioxide in the atmosphere and causes warming.

Test yourself

1 Give two ways in which P-waves are different from S-waves.

2 How does the destruction of the ozone layer increase the risk of skin cancer?

3 Someone who normally burns after 12 minutes in the Sun applies a sunblock with an SPF of 15. How long could they now stay in the Sun without getting burned?

4 How may global warming result in the extinction of some plants and animals?

5 The graph shows how global temperatures have changed since 1860.

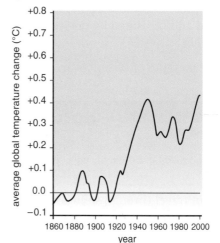

(a) What was the average global temperature change in 1860?

(b) What was the average global temperature change in 2000?

(c) The rate of average global temperature change has increased between 1860 and 2000. Use the graph to help you describe this increase.

(d) Suggest and describe one natural phenomenon that may have caused this increase.

(e) Suggest and describe one human activity that may have caused this increase.

P2a Collecting energy from the Sun

Photocells

One way of making use of energy from the Sun (solar energy) is with a **photocell**. This transfers light energy into electrical energy as follows:

1 Light falls on the silicon crystals in the photocell.
2 This gives enough energy to the electrons in the silicon to separate them from the atoms.
3 The electrons can then move freely.
4 If connected to a circuit the electrons will flow as an electrical current, transferring energy as they do so.

Photocells produce **direct current** (DC). This is electric current that flows in the same direction all the time.

The amount of electrical energy produced per second, the **power**, depends on:

● the surface area of the photocell that is exposed to light
● the intensity of the light.

Single photocells are used to power devices such as watches and calculators. If a large amount of power is required, many photocells are linked together.

Pros and cons of photocells

There are many advantages to using photocells:

Disadvantages include:

● The conversion of light energy into electrical energy only takes place in sunlight (or thin cloud cover) – no power is produced at night or if the weather is very bad.
● Single cells only produce small amounts of power.

Sometimes photocells are used to charge a battery. This transfers the electrical energy to chemical energy so it can be stored. We can then use the battery to power electrical devices when it is dark.

How science works

Photocells can be used to produce power where there is no mains supply but plenty of sunlight, such as in remote villages in hot countries.

They are also used to power satellites in space where a power supply is needed, but taking fuel or enough batteries from Earth would increase the weight of the satellite.

Solar heating

Some houses have passive solar heating. It works like this:

1 A glass wall is built on the sunny side of the house (usually the south side) with a space between it and the house wall.
2 Glass is transparent to light, so sunlight passes through the glass and is absorbed by the wall, which re-emits the energy as infrared radiation.
3 The infrared radiation is reflected by the glass and heats the surrounding air.

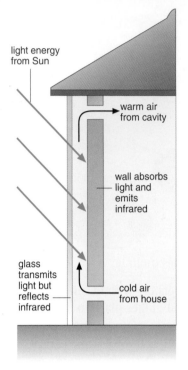

light energy from Sun

warm air from cavity

wall absorbs light and emits infrared

glass transmits light but reflects infrared

cold air from house

Solar cooking

Sunlight falling on a curved mirror is reflected and can be focused on an object such as a cooking pot. The pot absorbs the light energy and heats up, cooking the food inside.

For the device to be efficient the position of the mirror must be adjusted to track the position of the Sun in the sky so the light stays focused in the correct place.

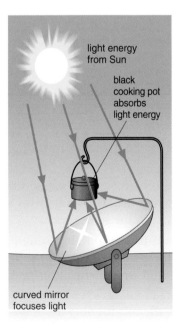

light energy from Sun

black cooking pot absorbs light energy

curved mirror focuses light

How science works

A solar furnace uses a very large number of curved mirrors all focused on one spot. This produces temperatures high enough to boil water and produce steam, which is then used to drive turbines which generate electricity.

The furnace can only generate electricity when the Sun is shining, and a large area is needed for the mirrors.

Exam tip

Make sure that you can explain how different devices used to convert solar energy to other forms are made as efficient as possible.

Wind power

Heat energy from the Sun creates convection currents in the air around us, making the air move as winds. The moving air has kinetic energy (KE). Devices called wind turbines are used to transfer the kinetic energy to electrical energy.

There are advantages and disadvantages to using **wind turbines** to generate electricity:

Advantages	Disadvantages
use a renewable energy source	their output is dependent on the wind speed
are tough	many are needed to produce the same output as a conventional power station, taking up lots of space
do not produce waste pollution	produce visual and noise pollution

Exam tip

Remember that although wind power is a renewable energy resource it has several disadvantages.

1 Why can solar energy be called a 'renewable' energy resource?

2 What is the energy transfer that takes place in a photocell?

3 A student is investigating photocells. She wants to know how the voltage produced by a set of photocells depends on the surface area exposed to sunlight. She measures the voltage with a voltmeter.

   (a) Suggest how the student could vary the amount of light reaching the photocells.
   (b) What should she do to make her results reliable?
   (c) What variable must the student try and keep the same to ensure a fair test?

4 Why are many wind turbines needed to produce the same output as a conventional power station?

5 Wind farms are often sited in remote locations on hilltops and on the coast. Suggest why.

P2b Generating electricity

After revising this item you should:

● be able to explain how electricity is generated in a power station, calculate the efficiency of this process and explain how electricity is distributed using the National Grid.

The dynamo effect

If a magnet is moved past a coil of wire, or a coil of wire is moved past a magnet, a voltage is produced across the ends of the wire. If the wire is part of a complete circuit a current will flow. We call this the **dynamo effect**.

You can increase the size of the voltage (and current) by:

● using a stronger magnet
● increasing the number of turns on the coil
● moving the magnet or the coil faster.

Exam tip

Be careful in the exam: using a stronger magnet is not the same as using a bigger magnet.

Generator

In a simple **generator** a magnet spins inside a coil of wire wound on an iron core. As the magnet spins it changes the **magnetic field** in the iron core, producing a voltage across the ends of the coil.

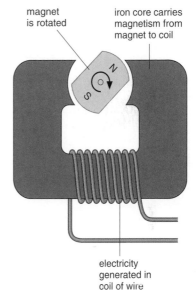

magnet is rotated

iron core carries magnetism from magnet to coil

electricity generated in coil of wire

A generator can also be made by spinning a coil of wire inside a stationary magnetic field.

A generator produces **alternating current** (AC). The direction of the voltage continuously changes so the direction of the current continuously changes. The number of cycles per second is called the frequency of the AC.

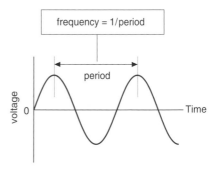

frequency = 1/period

period

voltage

0

Time

Power stations

Many power stations burn fuel, such as coal, oil or gas, to produce heat. This is used to turn water into steam. The steam passes through a turbine, forcing it to spin. The shaft of the turbine is connected to a generator, which turns and produces electricity.

In many power stations much of the energy from the burning fuel is wasted in heating the surroundings.

How science works

Some power stations use their wasted heat energy to heat surrounding buildings. However, in the UK this is not common and heat energy is usually just wasted to the air.

Is it sensible to waste energy and money in this way?

Who should pay to build the devices needed to make use of the energy?

Efficiency

For a power station

fuel energy input	=	waste energy output	+	electrical energy output

The efficiency of a power station can be calculated using the equation

$$\text{efficiency} = \frac{\text{electrical energy output}}{\text{fuel energy input}}$$

The National Grid

All the electricity produced in power stations in the UK is fed into a system called the **National Grid**. This is a network of cables that links power stations to consumers such as homes, schools, shops, offices, factories and farms.

Electricity is transmitted across the National Grid at a very high voltage. For any given power, increasing the voltage decreases the current. This reduces the heating of the cables, and so decreases energy waste. The voltage is increased to several hundred thousand volts by step-up **transformers**.

It would be dangerous to supply electricity to consumers at these very high voltages, so the voltage is reduced to 230 volts by a step-down transformer before it reaches consumers.

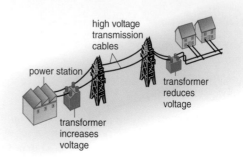

This flow chart summarises the stages in the production of electricity.

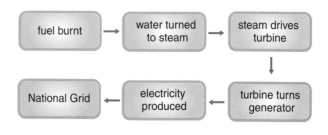

Exam tip

*Make sure you can explain each stage in the production of electricity and put them in the correct order: Fuel, Steam, Turbine, Generator, Electricity, National Grid. You could use a mnemonic like: **F**ind **S**omewhere **T**o **G**o **E**very **N**ight **G**irls, or make up your own.*

Test yourself

1 The magnet in a generator is spun faster. Describe what happens to the output voltage of the generator.

2 A power station produces 300 J of electrical energy for each 1000 J of energy obtained from the fuel it burns. What is the efficiency of the power station?

3 A power station has an efficiency of 0.5. How much fuel must be input for every 100 J of electrical energy output?

4 Why is the National Grid a better way to supply electricity than having a particular power station for each area?

5 Explain why electricity is transmitted across the National Grid at very high voltages.

P2c Fuels for power

After revising this item you should:

- be able to compare the advantages and disadvantages of common energy sources used in power stations, understand how energy is released from them and calculate the power of and energy used by an appliance.

Heat energy from fuels

The heat energy required to turn water to steam in a power station can be supplied in a number of different ways:

- Fossil fuels such as coal, crude oil and natural gas can be burned.
- Renewable **biomass** such as wood, straw and manure can be burned.
- **Uranium** atoms can be split into smaller atoms, releasing heat in a nuclear power station.
- Biomass can be fermented to produce methane gas, which can be burned.

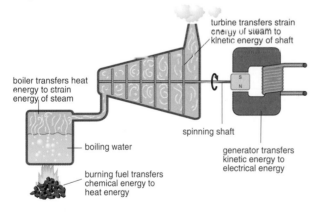

turbine transfers strain energy of steam to kinetic energy of shaft

boiler transfers heat energy to strain energy of steam

boiling water

spinning shaft

generator transfers kinetic energy to electrical energy

burning fuel transfers chemical energy to heat energy

The table shows the pros and cons of using fossil fuels:

Advantages	Disadvantages
reliable source of energy	non-renewable source of energy
do not depend on the weather or the time of the day to produce electricity	burning fossil fuels releases carbon dioxide, a greenhouse gas
gas power stations can be started up quickly at times of sudden demand	burning coal and oil releases sulfur dioxide, producing acid rain

Power

The amount of electrical energy that an appliance uses depends on:

- its power
- the length of time it is switched on.

The power of an appliance is usually given on the appliance. Or it can be calculated using the equation:

$$\text{power (W)} = \text{voltage (V)} \times \text{current (A)}$$

The unit of power is the **watt** (W), or the **kilowatt** (kW).

$1\,kW = 1000\,W$

Paying for electricity

Companies that supply mains electricity charge customers for the amount of electrical energy used. This is measured in **kilowatt-hours** (kWh). A kilowatt-hour is:

- the amount of energy that is transferred by a one kilowatt device when used for one hour.

You can calculate the energy used by an appliance, in kilowatt-hours, using the equation:

$$\text{energy (kWh)} = \text{power (kW)} \times \text{time used (hours)}$$

The electricity meter in a house records the number of kilowatt-hours of energy used. The energy used between readings is found by subtracting the previous meter reading from the current reading.

The cost of the electricity can be found using:

$$\text{cost} = \text{number of kilowatt-hours} \times \text{cost per kilowatt-hour}$$

The cost per kilowatt-hour depends on the time of day and how the electricity is generated.

For example, a student irons with a 1400 W iron for 30 minutes. If electricity costs 9p per kilowatt-hour how much does it cost to use the iron?

$$\text{Energy used} = 1.4\,\text{kW} \times 0.5\,\text{h} = 0.7\,\text{kWh}$$
$$\text{Cost} = 0.7\,\text{kWh} \times 9\text{p} = 6.3\text{p}$$

Exam tip

Take care with units when making these sorts of calculations. Remember that a kilowatt-hour is a unit of energy.

Nuclear power

Nuclear power stations use uranium as their fuel. Uranium is a non-renewable resource.

Nuclear fuel waste contains **plutonium**. It is radioactive and can be used to make nuclear bombs.

Advantages of nuclear power	Disadvantages of nuclear power
current uranium stocks are plentiful	high cost of building, maintaining and decommissioning nuclear power stations
does not rely on fossil fuels which are running out	risk of a serious accident releasing **radioactive material** into the atmosphere
does not produce carbon dioxide or contribute to global warming	transport, storage and disposal of radioactive nuclear waste is difficult and expensive

How science works

Nuclear power stations produce waste which can remain radioactive for thousands of years. This means that their use now produces waste that future generations will have to deal with.

Who do you think should decide whether or not to build nuclear power stations?

Test yourself

1 Give three advantages of using fossils fuels in power stations to generate electricity.

2 Calculate the current drawn from the 230V mains supply by a kettle of power 1800W.

3 Calculate the cost of using a 2300W heater for 90 minutes if electricity costs 7p per kilowatt-hour.

4 A kettle of power 1500W takes 6 minutes to boil when full. Each kilowatt-hour costs 10p. Calculate the cost of boiling the kettle.

5 Describe how uranium is used in a nuclear power station to generate electricity.

P2d Nuclear radiations

After revising this item you should:

● recall the three nuclear radiations and some of their uses, describe how to handle them safely and explain the problems of dealing with radioactive waste.

Nuclear radiation

Some materials give out **nuclear radiation** from the nuclei of their atoms. These are called radioactive materials. The three types of nuclear radiation are:

● **alpha** particles
● **beta** particles
● **gamma** rays

Ionisation

When nuclear radiations travel through a material they are able to knock electrons off the atoms causing other particles to gain electrons; this produces particles called ions. We call the process **ionisation**. The more ionisation that takes place the more quickly the energy of the nuclear radiation is used up, so the less distance it will penetrate into the material.

alpha particles	• the most ionising • the least penetrating • stopped by a few centimetres of air • stopped by a thin sheet of paper
beta particles	• less ionising than alpha but more ionising than gamma • more penetrating than alpha but less penetrating than gamma • stopped by a few metres of air • stopped by a thin sheet of metal
gamma rays	• the least ionising • the most penetrating • partially absorbed by several metres of concrete • partially absorbed by several centimetres of lead

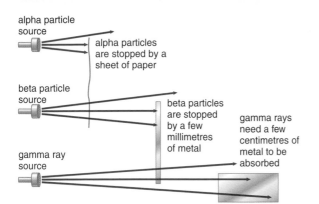

alpha particle source — alpha particles are stopped by a sheet of paper

beta particle source — beta particles are stopped by a few millimetres of metal

gamma ray source — gamma rays need a few centimetres of metal to be absorbed

Uses of nuclear radiation

Alpha particles are used:

- in smoke detectors. They cause ionisation of the air in the detector so that it conducts electricity and a small current flows. Smoke absorbs the alpha particles, the current is reduced and the alarm sounds.

Beta particles are used:

- by manufacturers of paper. The source is placed on one side of a continuous sheet of paper and a detector on the other. Changes to the thickness of the paper cause a change in the count rate detected.
- as tracers in medicine to allow doctors to monitor parts of the body without the need for surgery.

Gamma rays are used:

- to treat cancers. Beams of gamma rays from a source outside the body can kill tumour cells inside the body without the need for surgery.
- to kill bacteria on hospital equipment, sterilising it without the need for heating
- for non-destructive testing of welds in metals. If a gamma source is placed on one side of the weld and a photographic film on the other, any weak points in the weld will show up on the film.

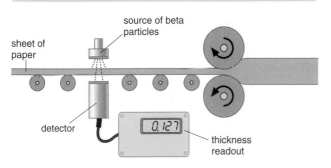

sheet of paper — source of beta particles — detector — thickness readout — 0.127

Exam tip

Make sure that you can relate the penetrating power of each radiation to its uses.

How science works

Gamma radiation can be used to kill bacteria in food such as fruit and vegetables. This stops it rotting so the fruit lasts longer, although it may taste different.

Some people object to this; they may think that it makes their food radioactive.

Should food be labelled so that people know if it has been treated?

Hazards of nuclear radiation

All nuclear radiations can be harmful to people. They cause ionisation in living cells. This may result in the cell undergoing cancerous changes or being killed.

Radioactive materials must be handled safely.

- Sources of radiation should be handled with tongs and kept away from the body.
- Exposure times should be kept as short as possible.
- People who work with nuclear radiation should wear film badges to monitor their exposure.
- Gloves and protective clothing should be worn.
- Sources must be stored safely, in clearly labelled, shielded containers.

Exam tip

Remember that the more penetrating the radiation the more dangerous it is outside the body and the more shielding we need to protect ourselves from it.

Background radiation

Background radiation is radiation that is around us all the time. It is caused by radioactive substances in rocks, soil and living things and **cosmic rays** from outer space.

Disposing of radioactive waste

We can dispose of **radioactive waste**, such as from a nuclear power station, in a number of ways.

- Low level waste can be buried in landfill sites.
- High level waste can be encased in glass and stored underground.
- Some of the waste can be reprocessed to make new fuel.

The waste is a big problem because:

- it emits harmful nuclear radiation
- some of the waste will remain radioactive for thousands of years
- there is always a risk that terrorists may use the waste to make nuclear bombs
- the waste cannot be allowed to enter groundwater supplies
- the level of radioactivity that is acceptable may change over time.

Test yourself

1 Why is using an alpha source in a smoke alarm not dangerous to people?

2 Why is beta radiation used to monitor paper thickness rather than alpha or gamma?

3 What is meant by ionisation?

4 Suggest why gamma rays are the most dangerous type of radiation outside the body.

5 Suggest why alpha particles are the most dangerous source of radiation inside the body.

P2e Our magnetic field & P2f Exploring our Solar System

After revising these items you should:

- be able to explain how scientists think the Earth's magnetic field comes about, describe our Solar System and explain the advantages and disadvantages of different types of space flight.

Magnetic fields

A magnetic field is a region where magnetic materials (such as iron and steel) will experience a force.

A plotting compass shows the direction of a magnetic field. All magnets have a north and a south pole. The Earth is surrounded by a magnetic field and this field has a north and a south pole.

A current is a flow of charged particles. An electric current in a coil of wire creates a magnetic field.

The shape of the Earth's magnetic field is like the shape of the one around a coil of wire when it is carrying a current.

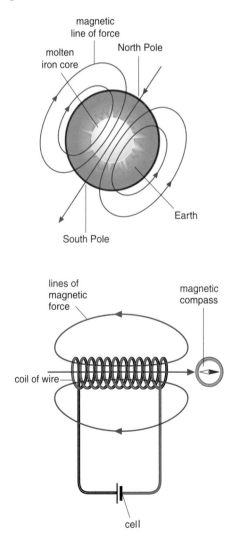

The core of the Earth contains a lot of molten iron. Scientists think that the magnetic field is made by large electric currents set up in the core as the Earth spins on its axis.

Cosmic rays

Cosmic rays are fast moving particles from outer space. When they hit the upper atmosphere they cause the production of gamma rays. Gamma rays may ionise materials that they pass through, so they can damage living organisms, causing cancer.

As the cosmic rays are charged, they are deflected by the Earth's magnetic field. They spiral around the lines of the Earth's magnetic field to the poles. The Aurora Borealis, or Northern Lights, seen in the night sky near the North Pole is caused by these cosmic rays.

Formation of the Moon

Scientists think that the Moon may be the result of a collision between the Earth and a large planet, billions of years ago.

- The two planets collided.
- The heavy iron from the cores of both planets merged to create the Earth.
- Less dense material merged to form the Moon.
- The Moon now orbits the Earth.

We can summarise the evidence for their ideas like this:

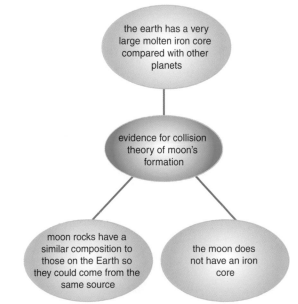

Solar flares

Solar flares:

- are clouds of charged particles ejected at high speed from the Sun
- create strong magnetic fields
- have sufficient energy to destroy the electronic circuits in orbiting satellites if the flares get close enough to the Earth
- produce surges of magnetism which can cause pulses of current to flow in large metal loops, such as those formed by electricity distribution networks. This can burn out transformers cutting off the supply.

The Solar System

The Earth is one of the **planets** that orbit the Sun and together form the Solar System. The closer the planet the shorter the orbit time. Mercury is the planet closest to the Sun. The order of the planets is Mercury, Venus, Earth, Mars, Jupiter, Saturn, Uranus, Neptune and Pluto.

Anything moving in a circle requires a **centripetal force** towards the centre of the circle. Gravitational force provides the centripetal force that keeps the planets in orbit around the Sun, and the Moon in orbit around the Earth.

The Universe and space travel

The Universe consists of billions of **stars**. Large groups of stars are called galaxies. The Universe also contains **comets**, meteors and **black holes**.

To explore other parts of the solar system and beyond we need to send out **spacecraft**.

There are many difficulties associated with sending people into space in manned spacecraft, such as providing enough:

• food and water • oxygen • warmth • fuel

Using unmanned spacecraft has several advantages:

• They do not need water, food or oxygen.
• They do not put the health of humans at risk.
• They can withstand conditions that would kill humans.

But there is no-one onboard to carry out maintenance during a mission.

Unmanned spacecraft can be used to give us information about other planets, including:

• temperature, magnetism and radiation
• gravity and atmosphere.

Because of the vast distances involved, even electro-magnetic radiation such as light and radio waves takes a long time to travel though the Solar System.

A **light-year** is the distance light travels in a year. It is used as the unit of measurement for the very large distances in space.

How science works

The low gravity experienced in space is very bad for human health. Without the stress of walking, running and jumping the bones rapidly lose mass and become liable to breakage.

Scientists are looking for ways to overcome this problem by producing artificial gravity to mimic conditions on Earth.

Test yourself

1 Draw a sketch to show the shape of the magnetic field around a coil of wire carrying a current.

2 Describe how some scientists think the Moon may have been formed. Suggest why they cannot be certain their ideas are correct.

3 Describe three uses of artificial satellites.

4 Why are we able to see the planets even though they do not give out light?

5 Suggest why an unmanned spacecraft would cost less to use than a manned spacecraft for the same mission.

P2g Threats to Earth & P2h The Big Bang

After revising these items you should:

● know the difference between an asteroid and a comet, explain the evidence for the Big Bang theory and describe the life cycle of a star.

Asteroids

Asteroids are large rocks left over from the formation of the Solar System. Many of them orbit the Sun in the asteroid belt, between Mars and Jupiter. The belt is there because the huge gravitational pull of Jupiter stops the rocks joining together to form planets.

There are several pieces of evidence that large asteroids have collided with the Earth:

• Impact **craters** in the surface of the Earth.
• Layers of unusual elements, such as iridium, in rocks
• Sudden changes in the number of fossils in layers of rock that are next to each other, showing that the number of living creatures dropped suddenly.

Exam tip

Make sure you can explain the evidence that shows that large asteroids have collided with the Earth in the past.

Comets

Comets are balls of ice and dust that slowly orbit the Sun in large **elliptical** orbits far beyond the planets. The comet spends most of its time away from the Sun, but when it is close to the Sun it speeds up. Heat from the Sun melts the ice and a trail of debris forms a tail on the comet.

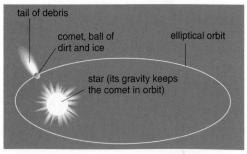

tail of debris

comet, ball of dirt and ice

elliptical orbit

star (its gravity keeps the comet in orbit)

Near-Earth Object (NEOs)

A **Near-Earth Object** is an asteroid or a comet on a collision course with Earth – it would cause enormous damage if it hit.

Astronomers search for NEOs with telescopes. They can track their paths with satellites and try to work out their trajectories. This is difficult, as the path of a NEO can be changed by the gravitational pull of another planet. If scientists thought that an NEO was likely to collide with Earth it is possible that causing an explosion nearby could deflect its path.

How science works

Scientists in the USA track the path of large asteroids in the northern hemisphere. If they find one on a collision course with Earth they will have to make a choice: should they warn people and risk causing panic or would it be better for the public not to know.

What do you think?

The origin of the Universe

The stars are grouped together in galaxies, each containing about a billion stars. Light from distant galaxies is shifted towards the red end of the spectrum. The further away the galaxy the bigger the red shift. This shows that all galaxies are moving away from us, and the distant galaxies are moving away quickest. This is true in every direction and suggests that the whole Universe is expanding outwards.

If the Universe is expanding it leads to the conclusion that it must have started with an explosion from a small initial point, or Big Bang. This is what we call the **Big Bang theory**.

The theory is supported because the Universe is filled with microwave radiation. Immediately after the Big Bang, the Universe was filled with very short wavelength gamma radiation. As the Universe cooled this became long wavelength microwave radiation.

We think that the Universe came into existence about 15 billion years ago.

The life cycle of stars

Exam tip

Look at the diagram below. To help you learn the life cycle of a star make a sketch to show each stage.

How science works

Optical telescopes collect light. Other telescopes collect electromagnetic waves from different parts of the spectrum, from gamma rays to radio waves. Scientists use information from all parts of the electromagnetic spectrum to develop their ideas about the Universe.

Test yourself

1 Describe the difference between an asteroid and a comet.

2 What evidence is there to suggest that large asteroids may have collided with the Earth in the past?

3 Describe one piece of evidence for the Big Bang theory.

4 Why is a black hole black?

5 Describe the stages in the life cycle of a star much bigger than the Sun.

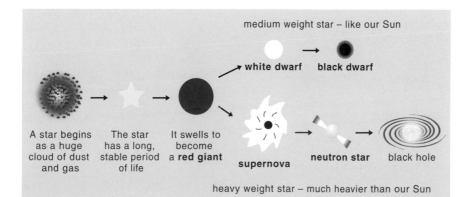

medium weight star – like our Sun

white dwarf   black dwarf

A star begins as a huge cloud of dust and gas

The star has a long, stable period of life

It swells to become a **red giant**

supernova

neutron star   black hole

heavy weight star – much heavier than our Sun

P3a Speed

After revising this item you should:

- be able to recall the relationship between speed, distance and time, calculate speeds, distances and times, and use distance–time graphs.

Calculating speed

Speed is measured in metres per second (m/s) or kilometres per hour (km/h).

Louise's car travels at a speed of 20 m/s. It will cover 20 metres in one second and 40 metres in two seconds.

At a faster speed of 30 m/s, she will cover a greater distance, 30 m, in each second and it will take less time to complete her journey.

To calculate speed you need to use this equation:

$$\text{speed} = \frac{\text{distance}}{\text{time}}$$

For example:

A cyclist travels 900 m in 1 minute. What is his speed in metres per second (m/s)?

distance = 900 m
time = 60 s
speed = ?
speed = $\dfrac{900\,\text{m}}{60\,\text{s}}$
= 15 m/s

If you are given the speed and either the distance or time you need to rearrange the equation. The following diagram shows a triangle that can help you remember how to do this.

$\text{speed} = \dfrac{\text{distance}}{\text{time}}$ $\text{time} = \dfrac{\text{distance}}{\text{speed}}$ $\text{distance} = \text{speed} \times \text{time}$

Step 1. You are given 'speed = distance over time' so write the equation in the triangle. When you cover up speed, distance is 'over' time.

Step 2. To find time, cover time and you have 'distance over speed'.

For example:

A car travels at 80 km/h. How long will it take to go 280 km?

speed = 80 km/h
distance = 280 km
time = ?
time = $\dfrac{\text{distance}}{\text{speed}}$
time = $\dfrac{280\,\text{km}}{80\,\text{km/h}}$
= 3.5 h

Exam tip

Always write down the rearranged equation you are using. You may get a mark for the equation but not the triangle.

Distance–time graphs

On a **distance–time graph**:

- a horizontal line means the object is stopped
- a sloping straight line means it has a steady speed
- a line curving upwards means the speed is increasing
- a line curving downwards means the speed is decreasing.

The steepness, or **gradient**, of the line shows the speed:

- A steeper gradient means a higher speed.

This graph is for a dog walking.

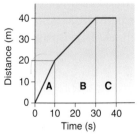

The following table shows the same information.

Section	Distance (m)	Time (s)	Speed (m/s)	Comment
A	20	10	2	
B	20	20	1	gradient not as steep as A, so speed is slower
C	0	10	0	stopped

Test yourself

1. In 2006 Asafa Powell held the 100 m world record with a time of 9.77 seconds. What was his speed?

2. If an athlete runs at a speed of 8 m/s how long will it take her to run 100 m?

3. Gareth drives his car at 50 km/h for 30 minutes, then at 80 km/h for 2 hours.

   (a) How far has he travelled?
   (b) Sketch a graph of the journey.

4. This graph shows different cycle rides.

   (a) Which cyclist cycled fastest?
   (b) Which cyclist stopped cycling?
   (c) Work out the speed that Chris and Joy cycled.

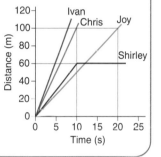

P3b Changing speed

After revising this item you should:

- be able to describe, draw and interpret speed–time graphs, and to calculate acceleration, speed and time.

Speed–time graphs

The diagram shows a **speed–time graph** for an off-road journey by a motorbike.

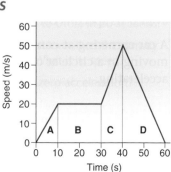

The gradient (steepness) of the graph is a measure of the acceleration. Part C is steeper than part A, so the acceleration is more in part C.

- In part A: the motorbike accelerates from 0 m/s to 20 m/s (a change of 20 m/s) in 10 s.
- In part C: the motorbike accelerates from 20 m/s to 50 m/s (a change of 30 m/s) in 10 s.

Distance on a speed–time graph

The distance travelled is shown on a speed–time graph by the area under the graph.

In part B of the graph (between 10 s and 30 s) the motorbike has travelled at a constant speed of 20 m/s for 20 seconds. The distance travelled is the area of the rectangle.

part B	time	=	20 s (between 10 s and 30 s)
	speed	=	20 m/s
	distance travelled in B	=	area of rectangle
		=	20 m/s × 20 s
		=	400 m
part A	the area of the triangle	=	half of rectangle
		=	20 m/s × 10 s
	distance travelled in A	=	area of triangle
		=	½ × 20 m/s × 10 s
		=	100 m
part C	The area is made of a triangle and a rectangle. 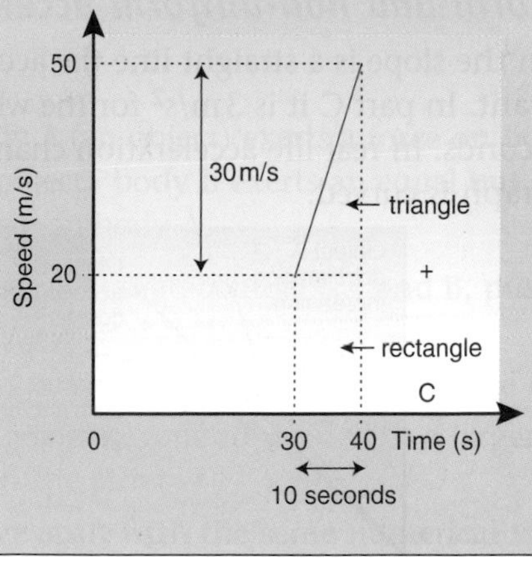		

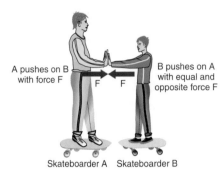

A pushes on B with force F

B pushes on A with equal and opposite force F

Skateboarder A   Skateboarder B

All forces come in interaction pairs. From the point of view of body A we feel B pushing. But body B feels A pushing. They are different views of the same interaction.

When a skateboarder pushes a wall, the wall pushes back with an equal and opposite force. The skateboarder moves away from the wall.

The wall does not move because forces from the ground balance the force from the skateboarder. These are balanced forces on the wall.

Exam tip

*The equal and opposite pair of interaction forces always act on **two different** objects. Balanced forces act on the **same** object.*

Stopping distances

$$\frac{\text{stopping}}{\text{distance}} = \frac{\text{thinking}}{\text{distance}} + \frac{\text{braking}}{\text{distance}}$$

This diagram shows the shortest stopping distances.

20 MPH	6 metres 6 metres	= 12 metres
40 MPH	12 metres 24 metres	= 36 metres
60 MPH	18 metres 55 metres	= 73 metres

Thinking distance
Braking distance

How science works

The Highway Code has a chart of shortest stopping distances like the one above that drivers have to learn to pass their driving test.

Driving safely includes:

- not driving too close to the car in front
- observing speed limits
- slowing down in poor road conditions.

Work done

Energy is transferred when **work** is done.

$$\text{work done (J)} = \text{force (N)} \times \text{distance (m)}$$

For example:

1. A man weighs 800 N. He climbs 10 m up a ladder. How much work has he done?

   work done = 800 N × 10 m = 8000 J

2. The braking force on a car is 6000 N. 576 000 J of work is done to stop the car. How far does it travel before it stops?

   $$\text{distance} = \frac{\text{work done}}{\text{force}}$$

   $$\text{distance} = \frac{576\,000\,\text{J}}{6000\,\text{N}}$$

   $$= 96\,\text{m}$$

work done

force   distance

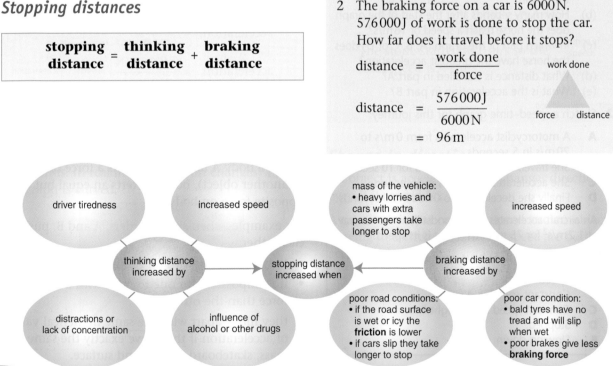

driver tiredness

increased speed

mass of the vehicle:
- heavy lorries and cars with extra passengers take longer to stop

increased speed

thinking distance increased by

stopping distance increased when

braking distance increased by

distractions or lack of concentration

influence of alcohol or other drugs

poor road conditions:
- if the road surface is wet or icy the **friction** is lower
- if cars slip they take longer to stop

poor car condition:
- bald tyres have no tread and will slip when wet
- poor brakes give less **braking force**

Power

$$\textbf{power } (W) = \frac{\text{work done (J)}}{\text{time (s)}}$$

For example:

1 A horse does 44 760 J of work pulling a cart for one minute. What power has it developed?

$$\text{power} = \frac{44\,760\,J}{60\,s}$$
$$= 746\,W$$

2 A 500 W pump is used to empty a pond. It does 600 kJ of work. How long did it take to empty the pond?

$$\text{time} = \frac{\text{work done}}{\text{power}}$$
$$\text{time} = \frac{600\,000\,J}{500\,W}$$
$$= 1200\,s \text{ (or (20 minutes)}$$

work done

power   time

Fuel consumption

The following table compares cars with petrol engines. The power of the engine increases with engine capacity.

Vehicle	Engine capacity (cc or cm^3)	CO_2 emitted (g/km)	Fuel consumption (litres/ 100 km)	Performance (mpg)
Vauxhall Corsa	998	115	4.8	58.8
Ford Focus	1596	180	7.5	37.7
Ford Galaxy	2792	288	12.0	23.5
Mitsubishi Shogun	3497	339	14.2	19.9
Lamborghini Diablo	5992	520	21.8	13.0

Source: Vehicle Certification Agency

Fuel consumption increases with engine power. Carbon dioxide emissions and other forms of pollution also increase.

How science works

Fuel consumption is measured in litres per 100 kilometres, so a low figure is better. Performance is given as miles per gallon and then a high figure is better.

Test yourself

1 (a) A car with mass 1400 kg accelerates at $5\,m/s^2$. What is the accelerating force?
   (b) A lorry with mass 3500 kg accelerates with a force of 7000 N. What is the acceleration?

2 A rowing boat drifts towards the bank of a lake. Explain, in terms of the forces on the bank and the boat, what happens when the rower pushes on the bank with an oar.

3 Use the chart of stopping distance (page 28) to compare:

   (a) the thinking distance, and
   (b) the braking distance

   at 20 mph and at 40 mph.

4 (a) Calculate the work done when a customer pushes a shopping trolley with a force of 8 N for a distance of 12 m.
   (h) 144 J of work is done pushing a second trolley 12 m. What is the pushing force?

5 An elephant does 48 000 J of work dragging a log for 75 s. The pulling force is 800 N.

   (a) How far does the elephant drag the log?
   (b) What power has the elephant developed?
   (c) How long would it take for a 800 W engine to do the same amount of work?

6 (a) Use the fuel consumption table opposite to explain how:
      (i) the emission of carbon dioxide is related to the power of the engine
      (ii) the fuel consumption changes as the power of the engine increases.
   (b) If petrol costs 90 p a litre how much does it cost to travel 100 km in:
      (i) the Mitsibushi Shogun
      (ii) the Vauxhall Corsa?

P3e Energy on the move & P3f Crumple zones

After revising these items you should:

- be able to work out kinetic energy, explain how it affects fuel consumption and braking distance, identify other factors that affect fuel consumption such as friction, driving speed and road conditions, and explain some safety features of modern cars.

Kinetic energy

All moving objects, e.g. vehicles, balls, animals and water, have **kinetic energy** (KE).

The kinetic energy is greater for objects with:

- higher speed
- greater mass (double the mass and you double the kinetic energy).

$$KE = \frac{1}{2}mv^2$$
where KE is kinetic energy (J)
m is mass (kg)
v is speed (v for velocity) (m/s).

Exam tip

You will be given this equation in the exam. Make sure you can use it. Do not forget to square the speed, or to multiply by a half. These are common mistakes.

For example:

What is the KE of a car of mass 1000 kg and speed 13 m/s?

$KE = \frac{1}{2} \times 1000\,kg \times (13\,m/s)^2 = 84\,500\,J$

Double the speed and the kinetic energy is four times as much, because it is squared.

For example:

What is the KE of the same car at 26 m/s?
$KE = \frac{1}{2} \times 1000\,kg \times (26\,m/s)^2 = 338\,000\,J$

Look at the braking distances in the shortest stopping distance chart on page 28:

- At 20 mph the braking distance is 6 m.
- At 40 mph the braking distance is 24 m.

When the speed of a car is doubled it has four times as much kinetic energy. At maximum braking force this means the braking distance is four times as far.

Fuel consumption

If a car is travelling at a steady speed it is still doing work against friction, so fuel is burned to supply the energy needed.

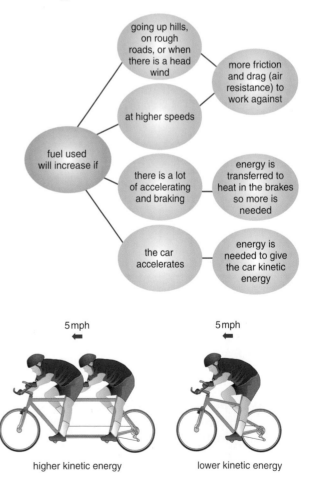

fuel used will increase if →
- going up hills, on rough roads, or when there is a head wind → more friction and drag (air resistance) to work against
- at higher speeds
- there is a lot of accelerating and braking → energy is transferred to heat in the brakes so more is needed
- the car accelerates → energy is needed to give the car kinetic energy

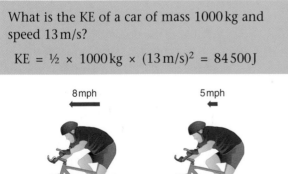

8 mph	5 mph
higher kinetic energy	lower kinetic energy

5 mph	5 mph
higher kinetic energy	lower kinetic energy

The following table shows fuel consumption for urban driving (stop-start city driving) and extra-urban driving (outside cities) for two different cars. The combined data is a cycle with some of both driving types. All cars have figures for these cycles which can be compared.

Car	Driving style	Fuel consumption (litres/100 km)	Performance (mpg)
Jaguar X-type	urban	7.7	36.6
	extra-urban	4.6	61.4
	combined	5.7	49.1
Renault Clio Campus	urban	7.4	38.2
	extra-urban	5.0	56.5
	combined	5.9	47.9

Source: Vehicle Certification Agency

Notice that the stop-start driving (urban cycle) uses more fuel. The Clio is intended for town driving. It has better consumption for this cycle than the Jaguar, but is not as good for the faster extra-urban driving.

Electric-powered cars

Fossil fuel (petrol, diesel and LPG) powered cars produce polluting gases including carbon dioxide.

Battery-powered cars:

- They do not give out exhaust gases so do not pollute at the point of use (on the roads).
- The batteries need recharging from an electricity supply.
- When this electricity is from a power station there is pollution produced at the power station.
- Batteries could be recharged from green sources such as solar or wind power.

Safety features

When a car stops, all the kinetic energy of the car, the driver, and the passengers must be safely transferred, e.g. to heat and sound. This is why brakes get very hot.

Allowing a long braking distance means that the braking force need not be so large. Escape lanes at the bottom of hills give extra distance for lorries to stop in an emergency.

It is the force, causing a large deceleration on the body, which causes injuries. We can reduce injuries by reducing the forces in a collision by:

- increasing the stopping or collision time
- increasing the stopping or collision distance
- decreasing acceleration (the acceleration in a collision is a deceleration, it needs to be kept as small as possible).

The following table show how forces are reduced in a collision.

Safety feature	Shape change	Absorb energy of	Increase collision time and distance	Driver and passengers decelerated more slowly
crumple zones	compressed	car	✓	✓
air bags	compressed	driver and passengers	✓	✓
seat belts	stretched	driver and passengers	✓	✓
crash barriers	compressed	car	✓	✓

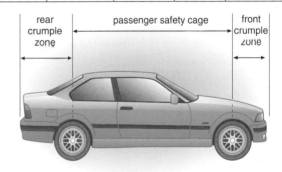

rear crumple zone — passenger safety cage — front crumple zone

Passive safety features

Here are some **passive safety** features of a car.

anti-lock braking system (ABS)	• helps you stop without skidding • a car that skids takes much longer to stop • to stop in the shortest distance a car needs the maximum friction force possible without skidding • sensors measure the friction force, and if the wheel is about to skid the braking force is reduced slightly, automatically, so the car does not skid
traction control	increases or decreases the force on each wheel to increase the grip and stop the car skidding
safety cage	a strong frame that keeps its shape and protects the driver and passengers in a crash

Active safety features

Here are some **active safety** features of a car.

easily accessible controls so the driver does not lose control of the car	• electric windows can be opened at the touch of a button • stereo controls near the steering wheel • paddle shift controls for the gears are fitted to racing cars and a few modern cars – pressing a button (or paddle) on the steering wheel changes the gear without moving a lever or pressing the clutch
cruise control	keeps the car at a steady speed less tiring for the driver and makes it easier to stick to the speed limit
adjustable seating	improves visibility and comfort

Test yourself

1 Which has the greatest kinetic energy (A or B):

  (a) A a train travelling at 20 mph or B a lorry travelling at 20 mph

  (b) A a car travelling at 50 mph or B the same car travelling at 70 mph?

2 Calculate the kinetic energy of a car with a mass of 1200 kg and a speed of 26 m/s.

3 Look at the braking distances in the chart on page 28. Use these to estimate the braking distance for a car travelling at 80 mph.

4 Chloe says that battery-powered cars do not pollute. Eshan says they do. Explain how they could both be right.

5 Adam is wearing a seatbelt when his car is involved in a collision.

  (a) How does the seatbelt reduce the force on Adam?

  (b) Give another example of a car safety feature that reduces injury in a collision.

P3g Falling safely

After revising this item you should:

● be able to explain why falling objects increase speed and reach a terminal speed.

Falling

Objects falling through the Earth's atmosphere accelerate. As they get faster the frictional force from the air increases and this reduces their acceleration. If they do not hit the ground first, objects reach a steady speed called **terminal speed**.

Why objects increase in speed

A falling object accelerates because of its weight. This force, caused by gravity, pulls it towards the centre of the Earth.

In the atmosphere the air pushes upwards against a falling object. This frictional force is called air resistance or **drag**. The diagram shows these forces on a skydiver.

start of dive

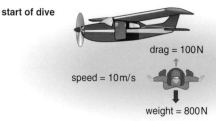

drag = 100 N

speed = 10 m/s

weight = 800 N

Drag (or air resistance) increases as the object moves faster. Weight stays the same. As the object moves faster the downward force accelerating the object gets smaller because:

> downward force = weight – drag

The acceleration gets smaller but the speed is still increasing.

Why objects maintain a steady speed

The speed and drag increase until the forces are balanced.

> weight = drag

There is zero downward force and zero acceleration.

The falling object is now moving at a steady speed. It is not accelerating, so the drag stays the same. The object will not slow down or speed up because the forces are balanced. This steady speed is called the terminal speed.

The diagram shows the skydiver has reached terminal speed.

terminal speed

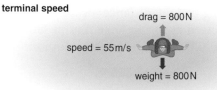

drag = 800 N

speed = 55 m/s

weight = 800 N

Using drag to decrease speed

Opening a parachute suddenly increases the drag because there is a large area for the air to push against. If the drag is larger than the weight the parachutist will slow down.

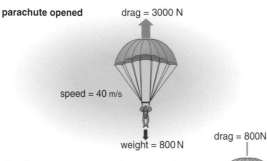

parachute opened

drag = 3000 N

speed = 40 m/s

weight = 800 N

drag = 800N

weight = 800N

The skydiver is slowing down and will eventually reach a new terminal speed as shown in the right-hand diagram.

The next diagram shows the speed–time graph for the whole jump.

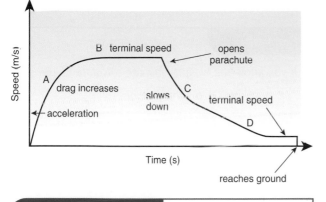

Speed (m/s)

B terminal speed

opens parachute

A

drag increases

slows down

C

terminal speed

acceleration

D

Time (s)

reaches ground

How science works

Parachute braking is used on jet-powered cars. When the parachute is opened behind the car the drag slows the car down.

Free-fall

If the only force on a falling object is its weight, it is in **free-fall**. The acceleration is constant, because there are no other forces. On Earth or in orbit this force is called 'g' force.

A steel ball and a feather, inside a glass tube with no air, will fall with the same acceleration and hit the ground at the same time.

Test yourself

1 Describe what happens to the speed and the drag force on a falling ball

(a) before it falls   (b)   when it is first dropped
(c) if it continues to fall for several seconds.

2 Look at the speed–time graph of a skydiver during a parachute jump (opposite). Draw diagrams to show the forces on the skydiver at points A, B, C and D and explain what is happening at each point.

3 Which of these statements (A–F) are true?

  A Falling objects increase speed when the drag is less than the weight.
  B If drag is larger than weight, falling objects can move upwards.
  C For objects at terminal speed, drag equals weight.
  D When a parachute opens the drag force can be larger than the weight.
  E The drag force depends on the speed of an object.
  F The drag force depends on the weight of an object.

4 An astronaut on the Moon drops a hammer and a feather from a height of 3 m above the surface. Which of these statements (A–D) is true?

  A The hammer weighs the same as the feather on the Moon.
  B There are no drag forces because there is no atmosphere.
  C The hammer and feather have no weight on the Moon.
  D The hammer and the feather are both in free-fall.

5 Explain how a parachute braking system can be used to slow down a car.

P3h The energy of games and theme rides

After revising this item you should:

● be able to calculate the gravitational potential energy of an object, explain that it can be converted to kinetic energy and back and explain how this is used in roller coasters, and be able to calculate the weight of an object.

Gravitational potential energy

- Water in a reservoir at the top of a hill has **gravitational potential energy** (PE). When the dam is opened the water flows downhill, gaining kinetic energy (KE). We can use this energy to turn the turbines of a hydroelectric power station.

- Alesha is on a trampoline. She goes up and slows down, losing KE and gaining the same amount of PE. At the top of the jump, for a moment, she is not moving. All the energy is PE. Then she starts to fall. The PE is converted back to KE so she gets faster and faster.

- As a skydiver falls he loses PE and gains KE until he reaches terminal speed. At terminal speed KE does not increase. There is a frictional force slowing the skydiver. The PE is used to do work against this force.

Gravitational field strength

On the Earth the **gravitational field strength** is six times greater than on the Moon.

The amount of PE an object gains by moving up on the Earth is six times greater than it would be if the object moved up the same distance on the Moon.

Potential energy is greater when the gravitational field strength is greater.

Calculating weight

On Earth all objects with mass are attracted downwards by gravity. We call the force on them weight.

Use this formula to find weight:

$$\frac{\text{weight}}{\text{(N)}} = \frac{\text{mass}}{\text{(kg)}} \times \frac{\text{gravitational field strength}}{\text{(N/kg)}}$$

On the Earth, g = 10 N/kg.

> **Exam tip**
>
> *You will always be given this value for g in the exam.*

For example:

1. Sophie has a mass of 55 kg. What is her weight?

   W = 55 kg × 10 N/kg
      = 550 N

2. The weight of an airliner is 5 600 000 N. What is its mass?

   Mass = $\dfrac{\text{weight}}{\text{gravitational field strength}}$

       = $\dfrac{5\,600\,000\,\text{N}}{10\,\text{N/kg}}$

       = 560 000 kg

Calculating potential energy

$$\frac{\text{gravitational}}{\text{potential}} = \frac{\text{mass}}{\text{(kg)}} \times \frac{\text{gravitational}}{\text{field strength}} \times \frac{\text{height}}{\text{(m)}}$$
$$\text{energy (J)} \qquad\qquad \text{(N/kg)}$$

PE   = mgh

> **Exam tip**
>
> *If you know the weight, you can calculate PE using*
>
> *PE = weight × height change*

For example:

Louise has a mass of 50 kg and climbs 60 m to the top of a monument. How much PE has she gained?

Using g = 10 N/kg
PE = 50 kg × 10 N/kg × 60 m
     = 30 000 J

How high would she have to climb to gain 10 000 J?

h = $\dfrac{\text{PE}}{\text{mg}}$

  = $\dfrac{10\,000\,\text{J}}{50\,\text{kg} \times 10\,\text{N/kg}}$

  = 20 m

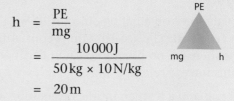

Roller coaster rides

1 A motor is often used to move the car to the top of a slope – giving it PE.

2 The car then travels down the slope, gaining KE and losing PE.

3 The car goes up the next slope, losing KE and gaining PE.

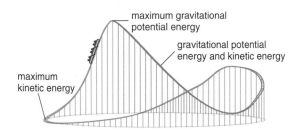

maximum gravitational potential energy

gravitational potential energy and kinetic energy

maximum kinetic energy

For example:

1 A roller coaster car with mass 2000 kg starts at the top of a 50 m slope. What is its speed at the bottom? (Use g = 10 N/kg.)

$$
\begin{aligned}
\text{PE lost} &= mgh \\
&= 2000\,\text{kg} \times 10\,\text{N/kg} \times 50\,\text{m} \\
&= 1\,000\,000\,\text{J}
\end{aligned}
$$

$$
\begin{aligned}
\text{KE gained} &= \text{PE lost} \\
\tfrac{1}{2}mv^2 &= 1\,000\,000\,\text{J} \text{ (see page 30 for the equation for KE)} \\
v^2 &= \frac{2 \times 1\,000\,000\,\text{J}}{2000\,\text{kg}} \\
&= 1000\,\text{J/kg} \\
v &= 31.6\,\text{m/s}
\end{aligned}
$$

2 The KE of a roller coaster car at the bottom of a slope is 1 200 000 J. The mass of the car is 1500 kg and its speed at the top was 0 m/s. How high was the slope? (Use g = 10 N/kg.)

PE lost = KE gained
PE lost = mgh

1500 kg × 10 N/kg × h = 1 200 000 J
h = 80 m

More about kinetic energy

$KE = \tfrac{1}{2}mv^2$ (see page 30)

If the mass is 1 kg and the speed is 1 m/s
$KE = \tfrac{1}{2} \times 1 \times 1 \times 1 = 0.5\,\text{J}$

Doubling the mass doubles the KE:
$KE = \tfrac{1}{2} \times 2 \times 1 \times 1 = 1\,\text{J}$

Doubling the speed quadruples the KE:
$KE = \tfrac{1}{2} \times 1 \times 2 \times 2 = 4\,\text{J}$

Test yourself

1 Jessica pulls the swing to point A in the diagram. She lets it go without pushing and it swings down through point B and up to C. Which statements (A–D) are true?

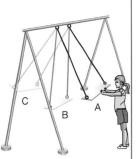

 A The swing has maximum PE at B.
 B The swing has maximum PE at A and C.
 C The swing has maximum KE at B.
 D The swing has maximum KE at A and C.

2 Which has the most PE, a 10 kg weight 6 m above the surface of the Earth or the same weight 6 m above the surface of the Moon?

3 A roller coaster car starts with a speed of zero at the top of a 20 m high slope. The car has a mass of 2000 kg.

 (a) Use the equation PE = mgh and g = 10 N/kg to work out the PE of the car at the top of the slope.
 (b) The car rolls down the slope. What happens to its PE?
 (c) Use the equation $KE = \tfrac{1}{2}mv^2$ to work out the speed of the car at the bottom of the slope.

4 (a) Car A has 90 000 J of KE. How much KE will it have if it travels at double the speed?
 (b) Car B travels at the same speed as car A, and has twice the KE. Why is this?

5 Using g = 10 N/kg, work out:

 (a) the weight of a 60 kg woman
 (b) the mass of a chocolate bar weighing 1 N.

P4a Electrostatic sparks

After revising this item you should:

- be able to explain electron movement and that electrostatic charges can attract and repel and cause electric shocks, and describe some of the dangers and problems they cause.

Electric charge

There are two types of electric charge: **positive charge** and **negative charge**.

- Materials that are positively charged have missing electrons.
- Materials that are negatively charged have extra electrons.

Like charges **repel** and unlike charges **attract**.

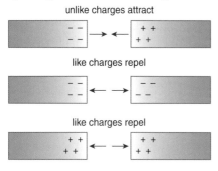

Electrostatic phenomena are caused by the transfer of electrons.

When insulators are rubbed, electrons are rubbed off one material and transferred to the other. This results in effects called electrostatic phenomena or **static electricity**.

Electric shocks

We feel a flow of electrons through our bodies because our nerves detect the flow. We call this an **electric shock**.

Electrostatic shocks are usually small and not harmful. Larger ones can be dangerous to people with heart problems. The flow of charge through the body can stop the heart.

Lightning is a very large electrostatic discharge. It can jump from a cloud to a building. If it flows through a body it is often fatal.

The earth connection

To discharge objects, or stop them becoming charged, we connect them with a thick metal wire to a large metal plate in the ground. This acts as a large reservoir of electrons. We call this an earth connection, and objects that are connected this way are said to be earthed.

Electrons flow so quickly to or from earth that earthed objects do not become charged. If all the metal water pipes in a house are connected into the ground like this they can be used as an earth.

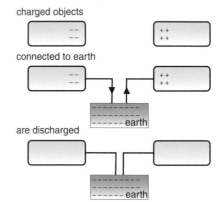

Electric shocks can also occur with electricity from batteries or the mains supply. The mains supply is much more dangerous than batteries or static. The metal cases of electrical appliances must be earthed to prevent electric shocks if there is a fault.

If you stand on an insulating mat you can become electrostatically charged more easily. When you step off the mat the charge will leak away through your shoes. If you wear shoes with insulating soles you will stay charged until you touch something that is earthed.

Dangerous static electricity

When an object is discharged the electrons jump across the gap just before the two objects touch. This is a spark. It can cause an explosion if:

- the atmosphere contains inflammable gases like hydrogen or methane
- there are inflammable vapours like petrol or methanol
- there is a high concentration of oxygen. This includes powders in the air, like flour or custard, which are carbohydrates. They contain lots of oxygen and burn easily. As a dust they can explode.

A nuisance

Small particles of dust and dirt are attracted to charged objects, for example:

- plastic cases
- TV monitors.

Clothing 'clings' to other items of clothing or to the body when it is charged, because it is attracted to oppositely charged or uncharged objects.

Anti-static sprays, liquids and cloths stop the build up of static charge and help reduce these problems.

Test yourself

1   When they are rubbed, what happens:
    (a)   to some materials to make them positively charged
    (b)   to other materials to make them negatively charged?

2   A polythene rod is rubbed with a duster and hung up on a piece of thread.
    (a)   What happens when a second rubbed polythene rod is brought close to it?
    (b)   When a perspex rod is rubbed and brought close to it, the polythene is attracted to the perspex. What does this tell you about the two materials?

3   Explain why is there a risk of explosion in a flour mill.

4   Explain why a petrol tanker must be earthed before it is unloaded.

5   (a)   Why does dust stick to television monitors?
    (b)   How can this problem be reduced?

P4b Uses of electrostatics

Defibrillators

A **defibrillator** is used to start the heart when it has stopped. It works because the flow of electric charge makes muscles contract.

1   Paddles are placed on the patients chest – they must make a good electrical contact.

2   Everyone including the operator must 'stand clear' so they don't get an electric shock.

3   The paddles are charged.

4   The charge is passed through the plates to make the heart contract.

Electrostatic dust precipitators

Electrostatic dust precipitators remove smoke particles from chimneys before they are carried out by the hot air and cause pollution. The precipitators make use of electrostatic charge to attract the smoke particles or dust.

1   Metal plates or grids are put in the chimneys.

2   They are charged by connecting them to a high potential difference (pd) or voltage.

3   The dust particles are attracted to the charged plates or grids.

4   They clump together on the plates to form larger particles.

5   When they are heavy enough, the dust particles fall back down the chimney into containers.

Depending on the design, dust can be:

- positively charged and attracted to negatively charged plates, or
- negatively charged and attracted to positively charged plates.

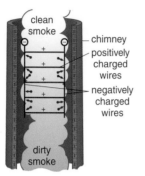

↘ charged dust particles attracted to plates

Paint spraying

Paint spraying can also make use of static electricity.

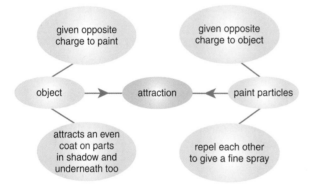

Test yourself

1 A defibrillator is used to restart a heart which has stopped beating.

   (a) Why is the patient's shirt undone and the paddles placed directly on the skin?

   (b) Why does the operator tell everyone to stand clear?

   (c) What effect does the charge have on the heart to make it start beating?

2 An electrostatic precipitator is installed in a chimney. The smoke particles pick up negative charge as they pass a negatively charged grid.

   (a) Why do the smoke particles travel up the chimney?

   (b) Name the particles that make the smoke particles negatively charged.

3 Smoke particles are attracted to charged plates in an electrostatic precipitator. They form a thick layer which falls off when the plates are hit with hammers.

   (a) What is the charge on the plates?

   (b) Why does the smoke layer fall down and not go up the chimney?

4 A paint spraying system uses opposite charges on the paint particles and the car body.

   (a) Explain what effect the electric charges have when paint is sprayed towards the car.

   (b) Explain why less paint is wasted using this system.

   (c) Give another benefit of the system.

5 Which of these statements (A–F) are true?

   A A defibrillator uses electric charge to make the heart contract.

   B A defibrillator could stop the heart if it is beating already.

   C An electrostatic paint sprayer uses the same charge on the paint and the object to be painted.

   D An electrostatic precipitator attracts smoke particles out of the top of a chimney.

   E In an electrostatic precipitator the smoke particles are given a charge.

   F In an electrostatic precipitator the charge on the plates is reversed to make the smoke particles fall off.

P4c Safe electric circuits

After revising this item you should:

- be able to explain how an electric circuit works, describe how a variable resistor can change the current in a circuit, calculate resistance and explain how fuses and circuit breakers make circuits safer.

Electric circuits

A flow of electric charge in a **circuit** is called a current. We can use variable resistors to change the current in a circuit.

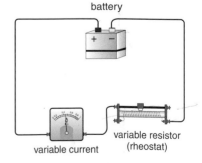

The **resistance** of a **variable resistor**, or **rheostat**, can be:

- increased by moving the slider to make the wire longer
- decreased by moving the slider to make the wire shorter.

When the resistance increases the current decreases.

How science works

Variable resistors are found inside joystick controls used for all kinds of things, from computer games to wheelchairs.

As you move the joystick back and forth you change the resistance of one variable resistor. For the side-to-side movement there is a second variable resistor.

Changing the resistance changes the current, so the position of the stick is translated into an electrical signal for the computer.

Current, potential difference and resistance

Current:

- passes **through** wires or components
- is measured in amperes or amps (A) using an ammeter.

Voltage or **potential difference** (pd):

- is set up **across** a wire or a component – between the two ends
- is measured in volts (V) using a voltmeter.

Exam tip

You must know these electric circuit symbols for the exam.

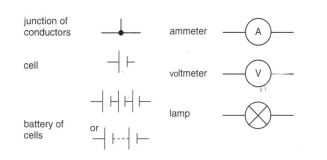

The circuit diagram shows a circuit used for two experiments.

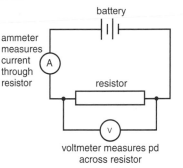

The first experiment uses the same resistor and different batteries.

- Increasing the pd across the resistor increases the current through it.
- Decreasing the pd across the resistor decreases the current through it.

Resistance:

The second experiment uses the same battery and different resistors.

When you have a fixed pd (e.g. a 9 V battery):

- increasing the resistance decreases the current
- decreasing the resistance increases the current.

To find resistance you use the formula:

$$\text{resistance (ohms)} = \frac{\text{voltage (V)}}{\text{current (A)}}$$

For example:

1 A 9 volt battery is connected to a resistor and the current is 0.9 amps. What is the resistance?

$$\text{resistance} = \frac{9\,\text{V}}{0.9\,\text{A}}$$
$$= 10 \text{ ohms}$$

2 A 100 ohm resistor is connected to the 240 V mains electricity supply. What is the current?

$$\text{current} = \frac{\text{voltage}}{\text{resistance}}$$
$$= \frac{240\,\text{V}}{100\,\text{ohms}}$$
$$= 2.4\,\text{A}$$

voltage

resistance   current
(If you need a reminder
of how to use the triangle,
see P3a Speed on page 24.)

Mains wiring

Wire	Colour	Purpose
live wire	brown	the high voltage connection
neutral wire	blue	second wire to complete the circuit
earth wire	yellow and green	safety wire to stop the appliance becoming live

A conductor is live when it is connected to the electricity supply by the live or neutral wire. If you touch it you get an electric shock that could be fatal.

Conductors, like the metal cases of appliances, cannot become live if they are connected to the earth wire.

Fuses and circuit breakers

A **fuse** is a thin piece of wire. It is a weak link in the circuit.

If the current gets too large, the fuse:

• will melt

• break the circuit and prevents the flow of current.

This prevents the flex overheating and causing fire which prevents further damage to the appliance.

Fuses will not stop you getting an electric shock – they take too long to melt. After it has melted the fuse must be replaced.

• A 2 amp fuse melts when a current of 2 amps flows through it.

• A 13 amp fuse melts when 13 amps flows through it.

You should fit the lowest fuse that will carry the normal operating current.

Circuit breakers are switches that switch the current off when it gets too high. They can be switched on again once the fault is corrected.

A residual current device (RCD) is a circuit breaker that switches off very quickly. It will protect you from receiving an electric shock.

Electric shocks, the fuse and the earth wire

Touching a live appliance could result in a fatal electric shock.

The fuse and the earth wire can be used together to prevent the metal casing of an electric appliance becoming live.

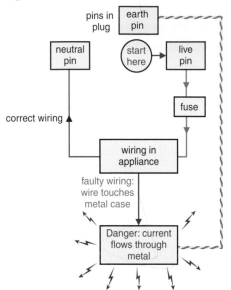

Use the diagram to help you follow what happens.

Circuit	Starts at	Route
correct	live pin of the plug	through the fuse ↓ through the appliance ↓ back to the neutral pin
faulty	live pin of the plug	through the fuse ↓ through the appliance ↓ through the faulty connection to the metal case ↓ through the metal case ↓ through the earth wire to the earth This will be such a huge current that it will melt the fuse and break the faulty circuit, stopping the current.

Double insulated appliances

Double insulated appliances do not need earthing because the case of the appliance is not a conductor, so it cannot become live.

Test yourself

1 (a) Vicky is changing the pd across a resistor, and measuring the current through it. Describe what happens to the current when she decreases the pd.

   (b) She keeps the pd constant and changes the resistor to one with higher resistance. What happens to the current?

2 The current in a light bulb is 0.4 A when it is connected to the 240 V mains supply. Work out the resistance of the light bulb.

3 (a) The current through a 2000 ohm resistor is 0.12 amps. What is the pd across the resistor?

   (b) The pd across a 300 ohm resistor is 9 volts. What is the current through it?

4 (a) How does a fuse protect the wires in an appliance from overheating?

   (b) Choose the correct fuse, either 3 amp or 13 amp, for each appliance:
     (i) A kettle with normal current 11 amps.
     (ii) A hairdryer with normal current 4 amps.
     (iii) A light bulb with normal current 0.4 amps.

5 (a) What is the advantage of using a circuit breaker instead of a fuse?

   (b) What is meant by a 'double insulated' appliance?

   (c) Why is the earth wire connected to the case of a metal appliance?

P4d Ultrasound & P4e Treatment

After revising these items you should:

● be able to describe features of longitudinal and transverse waves, recall that ultrasound is a longitudinal wave, compare X-rays and gamma rays and describe medical applications of ultrasound, beta radiation, gamma rays and X-rays.

Longitudinal waves

A longitudinal wave can be made to travel along a slinky spring. In a longitudinal wave the vibrations are back and forth, parallel to the direction of travel.

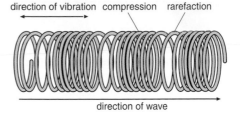

direction of vibration   compression   rarefaction

direction of wave

● **Compression** – where the particles are closest together (in the spring the coils are bunched together).

● **Rarefaction** – where the particles are furthest apart (in the spring the coils are spread out).

● Amplitude – the maximum distance a particle moves from its normal position (in the spring the maximum distance of a coil from where it would be if no wave disturbed it).

● Wavelength – the distance before the wave repeats (e.g. between two compressions or between two rarefactions).

● Frequency – the number of waves passing a point in one second (e.g. the number of compressions passing a point in one second).

The lines in this diagram represent layers of air particles. If there was no wave they would be evenly spaced.

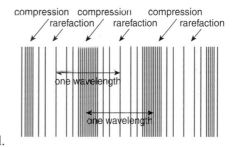

compression compression compression
rarefaction rarefaction rarefaction

one wavelength

one wavelength

The second type of wave is the transverse wave.

In a transverse wave the particles vibrate at right angles to the direction the wave is travelling.

Both longitudinal and transverse waves carry energy, but not material. The particles vibrate, moving:

● up and down   ● back and forward

● side to side

but the particles do not get carried along with the wave.

Ultrasound

Ultrasound is a longitudinal wave.

Ultrasound waves are sound waves with a frequency that is higher than the **upper threshold of human hearing**.

Ultrasound in medicine

body scans	the ultrasound beam is sent into the body. Each time it crosses a boundary between different tissues some is reflected. These reflections from different layers are built up into a picture by a computer.
	Ultrasound is reflected from soft tissues so it can detect things that X-rays cannot. It does not damage living cells like X-rays so it is safer.
breaking down stones	the vibrations caused by ultrasound waves can break down accumulations, e.g. kidney stones.

Nuclear radiation and X-rays

Beta radiation and **gamma rays** are used in nuclear medicine because they can pass through the skin. (Alpha radiation cannot.)

X-rays are easier to control than gamma rays.

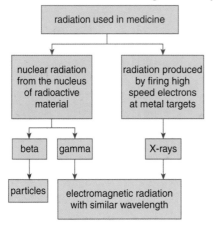

Cancer treatment

Alpha and beta radiation, and gamma and X-rays, can damage or kill living cells. There is always a risk in using them, but they can be beneficial.

Gamma rays are used to treat cancer:

- Gamma rays are focused on the tumour.
- A wide beam is used. This is rotated round the patient, keeping the tumour at the centre.
- The tumour receives a concentrated dose of gamma rays. The non-cancerous tissue gets a weak dose, which limits the damage

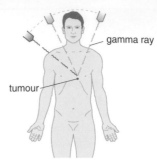

Treating a tumour with gamma rays.

Medical tracers

Radioactive medical **tracers** are materials that emit beta radiation or gamma rays.

A tracer is ingested by the patient. (The tracer could be drunk, eaten, injected or even breathed in as a gas.)

The doctors wait for the tracer to spread through the body. Different tracers are used for different parts of the body. Doctors choose a tracer that, once inside the body, is carried to the part they want to investigate.

The beta radiation (or gamma rays) pass out of the body. Doctors use a radiation detector to record them, e.g. a gamma camera.

How science works

When X-rays and radioactive materials were first discovered, all kinds of claims were made about the health benefits. There were some strange health treatments that exposed people to high doses. Some people suffered cell damage and cancer and some died.

Gradually evidence built up that this type of radiation was dangerous and safety precautions were introduced. In the 1950s all pregnant women were X-rayed. Today only essential X-rays are done.

Test yourself

1 (a) Describe how the particles move:
    (i) in a transverse wave
    (ii) in a longitudinal wave.
  (b) Describe what happens to the particles if the amplitude of the transverse wave increases.
  (c) What is meant by the wavelength of a longitudinal wave?

2 Explain how an ultrasound scan of a fetus is taken.

3 Describe one way that gamma rays are similar to X-rays and one way that they are different.

4 Which of these statements (A–G) are true?

   A   Gamma rays are used to treat cancer.
   B   Beta radiation does not damage living cells.
   C   X-rays can be used as tracers.
   D   Tracers are radioactive materials that emit beta radiation or gamma rays.
   E   Some tracers are drunk by the patient.
   F   A tracer is a beam of gamma rays fired at a patient.
   G   A gamma camera is used outside the patient to detect gamma rays emitted by the tracer inside the patient.

5 (a) Describe how the damage to a patient's healthy cells is kept to a minimum when a tumour is treated with gamma rays.
    (b) Describe how the risk to the radiographer is kept to a minimum.

P4f What is radioactivity?

After revising this item you should:

- be able to explain what is meant by radioactive half-life and describe what happens to a nucleus when an alpha particle or a beta particle is emitted.

Radioactive materials

Radioactive substances contain radioactive nuclei that **decay** naturally and emit nuclear radiation.

The nuclear radiation can be:

- alpha   • beta   • gamma

Half-life

Half-life is the average time for half of a sample of radioactive nuclei to decay.

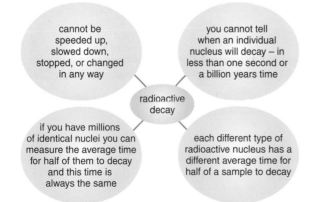

- cannot be speeded up, slowed down, stopped, or changed in any way
- you cannot tell when an individual nucleus will decay – in less than one second or a billion years time
- radioactive decay
- if you have millions of identical nuclei you can measure the average time for half of them to decay and this time is always the same
- each different type of radioactive nucleus has a different average time for half of a sample to decay

The following diagram shows a sample of radioactive nuclei with a half-life of 6 hours.

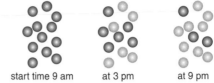

start time 9 am   at 3 pm   at 9 pm

● = one million radioactive nuclei ◯ = one million stable nuclei

After one half-life, half of the original nuclei are left. After two half-lives, one quarter of the original nuclei are left.

For example:

> A radioactive sample has a half-life of 5 hours. How long will it take for the count rate to drop from 60 counts per minute to 15 counts per minute?
>
> $$60 \times \tfrac{1}{2} = 30, \; 30 \times \tfrac{1}{2} = 15$$
>
> so it will take 2 half-lives = 2 × 5 hours
>   = 10 hours.

Radioactive decay is often plotted as a graph of radioactivity (the number of decays emitted per second) against time.

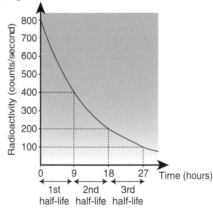

In the diagram the activity halves from 800 to 400 in 9 hours, so the half-life is 9 hours.

Notice that it also takes 9 hours to drop from 400 to 200.

To drop from 800 to 100 is three half-lives (one half of one half of one half = one eighth).

Alpha radiation

An **alpha particle** (also called **alpha radiation**) is:

- made up of two protons and two neutrons
- the same as a fast moving helium nucleus.

Alpha decay

An alpha particle is written $^4_2\alpha$.

This means:

- 2 protons: atomic number = 2
- 2 protons and 2 neutrons: mass number = 4.

For example, the diagram on the right shows what happens when radon decays by emitting an alpha particle.

$$^{219}_{86}Rn \longrightarrow {}^{215}_{84}Po + {}^4_2\alpha$$

The new nucleus is polonium. It has two less protons and two less neutrons than radon.

unstable nucleus

$\downarrow$

loses alpha particle:
2 protons +
2 neutrons

$\downarrow$

new element:
mass number down 4
atomic number down 2

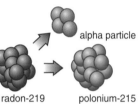
alpha particle

radon-219   polonium-215

Beta radiation

A **beta particle** (also called beta radiation) is:

- a very fast moving **electron**
- thrown out of the decaying nucleus.

The nucleus has no electrons – think of it as one neutron changing into a proton and an electron. The electron leaves as a beta particle and the proton stays in the nucleus.

unstable nucleus

$\downarrow$

loses beta particle:
negative charge
negligible mass

$\downarrow$

new element:
mass number unchanged
atomic number up 1

Beta decay

The new element has one more proton and one less neutron.

A beta particle is written $^0_{-1}\beta$.

For example, the diagram on the right shows what happens when carbon decays by beta radiation to form nitrogen.

$$^{14}_6C \longrightarrow {}^{14}_7N + {}^0_{-1}\beta$$

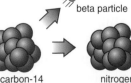
beta particle

carbon-14   nitrogen-14

How science works

The spent fuel from a nuclear reactor contains many different radioactive elements. Some of these have short half-lives and will quickly decay, but others will remain hazardous for thousands of years, and others for millions of years.

Reprocessing plants separate the products into fuel that can be reused and waste that must be safely stored.

Plutonium-239 has a half-life of 24 000 years. For the activity to fall to one eighth it would take three half-lives or 72 000 years.

Exam tip

Remember: alpha particles and beta particles are thrown out of decaying nuclei. Alpha particles are not helium atoms and beta particles are not electrons from the electron shell of an atom.

Test yourself

1 What is:

   (a) radioactive half-life   (b) an alpha particle
   (c) a beta particle?

2 Technetium-99 (Tc-99) has a half-life of 6 hours.

   (a) If there are 128 million atoms in a sample, how many are left after 7 half-lives?
   (b) How long does it take for the activity of a Tc-99 source to fall from 40 counts per minute to 10 counts per minute?
   (c) If a patient is injected with a dose of Tc-99, what fraction is left after 24 hours?

3 (a) Use this graph to complete the table below.

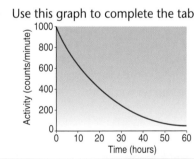

Activity (counts/min)	Time (hours)
1000	
	10
500	
	25

   (b) Use the table to decide the half-life of the source.

4 Uranium-238 decays by alpha emission to thorium.

(a) What happens to the protons and neutrons in the nucleus when an alpha particle is emitted?

(b) Copy and complete this equation for the decay.

$$^{238}_{92}U \longrightarrow {}^{?}_{?}\alpha + {}^{?}_{?}Th$$

5 Boron-12 decays by beta emission to carbon.

(a) What happens to the protons and neutrons in a nucleus when a beta particle is emitted?

(b) Copy and complete this equation for the decay.

$$^{12}_{5}B \longrightarrow {}^{?}_{?}\beta + {}^{?}_{?}C$$

P4g Uses of radioisotopes & P4h Fission

After revising these items you should:

● be able to explain where background radiation comes from and describe and explain some uses of radioactivity, including dating and nuclear reactors.

Background radiation

Background radiation is in the environment all the time. It is caused by radioactive substances and varies from place to place.

The diagram shows the different origins of background radiation.

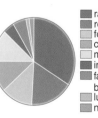

- radioactive gases
- rocks and soil
- food and drink
- cosmic rays
- medical
- industry
- fallout from atom bomb tests
- luminous paint etc.
- nuclear power

How science works

The nuclear industry is regulated and workers must have special training because of the risk to living cells from radiation.

Industrial use of tracers

A tracer can be used to detect a leak or a blockage in a pipe.

- The tracer is added to the fluid in the pipe.
- A gamma source is used so it can penetrate to the surface.

The diagram shows how the **gamma radiation** from the tracer shows where the leak is. Radiation is detected above X and Y, but is reduced, or not detected, at Z.

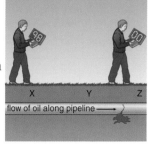

flow of oil along pipeline ⟶

Smoke detectors

Alpha sources are used in **smoke detectors**.

- Alpha particles from the source ionise atoms in the air (into electrons and positive ions) so that the air can conduct electricity.
- A small current flows and a sensor detects it.
- If smoke blocks the path of the positive ions and electrons, there is no current and the alarm sounds.

Radioactive dating

Rocks contain radioactive isotopes of uranium. The older the rock, the more of the isotope will have decayed to an isotope of lead. We can use the ratio of uranium to lead to date the rock.

Carbon dating

The amount of carbon-14 in the air has not changed for thousands of years.

The diagram shows how **carbon dating** is used to find the age of a once-living thing.

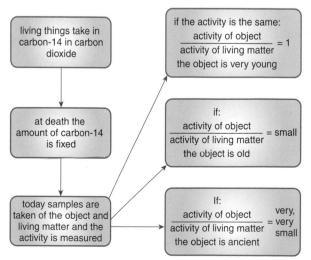

living things take in carbon-14 in carbon dioxide

at death the amount of carbon-14 is fixed

today samples are taken of the object and living matter and the activity is measured

if the activity is the same:
$$\frac{\text{activity of object}}{\text{activity of living matter}} = 1$$
the object is very young

if:
$$\frac{\text{activity of object}}{\text{activity of living matter}} = \text{small}$$
the object is old

If:
$$\frac{\text{activity of object}}{\text{activity of living matter}} = \text{very, very small}$$
the object is ancient

Nuclear power

Electricity is generated in a nuclear power station.

the nuclear reaction
produces heat

↓

the heat is used to
produce steam

↓

the steam turns a turbine,
which turns a generator

Nuclear fission

In the process of **nuclear fission**:

1. A uranium nucleus is hit by a neutron.
2. It absorbs the neutron and becomes unstable.
3. The unstable nucleus splits in two.
4. Energy is given out – this energy is harnessed in a nuclear reactor.
5. The two smaller nuclei produced are radioactive waste.

As each uranium nucleus splits, more than one neutron is given out. These neutrons can cause other uranium atoms to split and lead to a **chain reaction**.

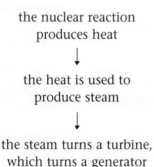

neutron

uranium atom

A nuclear bomb is a chain reaction that has run out of control.

Controlling nuclear reactions

A nuclear reactor has control rods made of a material that absorbs neutrons. Scientists lower the rods into the reactor to absorb some of the neutrons.

They allow just enough neutrons to remain to keep the process operating.

Useful isotopes and radioactive waste

When materials are placed in a nuclear reactor some of the nuclei absorb extra neutrons. This makes them radioactive.

Test yourself

1. Look at the diagram on page 45 showing sources of background radiation.

   (a) Estimate the fraction of background radiation from:
       (i) cosmic rays
       (ii) radioactive gases.
   (b) Explain why background is not the same everywhere.

2. (a) Which isotope is used to date objects that were once living?
   (b) How does the isotope get into:
       (i) living plants
       (ii) living animals.
   (c) Explain how the age of the object is worked out.
   (d) What has to remain constant for this method to work?

3. A sample of living bone has an activity of 60 counts per minute. Using the half-life of carbon-14 (= 5500 years) work out the age of these samples:

Sample	Activity (counts per minute)
X	30
Y	15
Z	60

4. Explain the following terms:

   (a) nuclear fission   (b) chain reaction
   (c) nuclear reactor   (d) control rods.

5. (a) Name a fuel used in a nuclear reactor.
   (b) What is needed to start the fission reaction?
   (c) Why does the reaction keep going?
   (d) How do scientists stop it going out of control?

P5a Satellites, gravity and circular motion

After revising this item you should:

- be able to describe the force of gravity, explain why satellites stay in orbit and describe different types of orbit and their uses.

Gravitational force

Gravity is a force of attraction that acts between all masses.

- The bigger the masses the bigger the force.
- The further apart the masses the smaller the force.

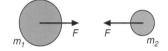

The Moon stays in orbit around the Earth, and the Earth stays in orbit around the Sun, because of the gravitational forces between them.

Period

The **period** of an orbit is the time taken to complete one orbit. The further a planet is from the Sun, the greater the period of the orbit.

Comets have very elliptical orbits around the Sun. When the comet is far from the Sun the gravitational force on it is less. It moves more slowly than when it is close to the Sun.

Satellites

Satellites are continuously accelerating towards the Earth because of the gravitational pull of the Earth. But as they fall towards the Earth its surface curves away beneath them – they are in orbit.

The Moon is a natural satellite of the Earth.

Artificial satellites also orbit the Earth. Gravity provides the centripetal force for orbital motion. (See P2f Exploring our Solar System, page 20.)

The lower the orbit of a satellite the:

- shorter the period of the orbit
- stronger the gravitational force on the satellite
- greater the speed of the satellite.

If a satellite was performing circular motion and the centripetal force was suddenly removed, the satellite would move away in a straight line at a **tangent** to the circle.

Geostationary orbits

Geostationary satellites are in a special orbit around the Earth called a **geostationary orbit**.

These satellites all orbit:

- above the equator
- with a period of 24 hours
- at a height of 35800 km
- above a fixed position on the Earth.

Geostationary satellites are used for:

- communications
- weather forecasting.

How science works

The geostationary orbit above the equator is filling up, with working satellites and old pieces of debris – 'space junk'.

How do we decide what should be allowed in the orbit and who should have permission to put it there?

Who could check that countries and companies are sticking to any agreements made?

Low polar orbits

Some satellites have much lower orbits than geostationary orbits.

The period of the orbit depends on the height of the orbit above the Earth. Low orbits can have a period of as little as a couple of hours.

If such an orbit passes over the Earth's poles it is called a **low polar orbit**.

As a satellite moves in a low polar orbit the Earth rotates beneath it. So over several orbits such a satellite is able to observe and image the whole surface of the Earth.

Satellites in low polar orbits can be used for:

- weather forecasting
- monitoring climate change
- spying.

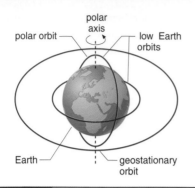

Exam tip

You need to remember the differences between geostationary and low polar orbits.

You can remember which orbit is high and which is low using 'goblins have peculiar legs' to remind you of 'geostationary high, polar low'. Or make up your own phrase.

Test yourself

1 (a) What force keeps a satellite in orbit?
   (b) What is the direction of this force?
   (c) What would happen to the path of a satellite if the force in (a) was suddenly removed?

2 Describe the main features of a geostationary orbit.

3 Two satellites, A and B, are in orbit around the Earth.

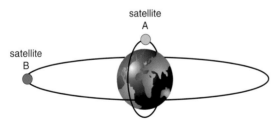

satellite A

satellite B

Which satellite:

   (a) is travelling faster?
   (b) takes the longer time to complete one orbit?
   (c) has the larger gravitational force acting on it?

4 Suggest three uses for a satellite in a low polar orbit.

5 A comet has an elliptical orbit around the Sun. Describe how the gravitational force on the comet and the speed of the comet vary as it completes one orbit.

P5b Vectors and equations of motion & P5c Projectile motion

After revising these items you should:

- be able to explain the difference between scalar and vector quantities, determine the resultant of two vectors and use the equations of uniformly accelerated motion, including their application to the motion of projectiles.

Scalars and vectors

Scalars are quantities that have magnitude (size) only.

Example of scalars are:

- distance
- speed
- energy
- mass
- time

Vectors are quantities that have magnitude and an associated direction.

Examples of vectors are:

- displacement
- velocity
- momentum
- force
- acceleration

Velocity is speed in a given direction.

If you say that you are travelling at:

- 1 m/s, you are stating your speed
- 1 m/s due north, you are stating your velocity.

Resultants

One or more vectors acting together can be replaced by a single vector that has the same effect. The single vector is called the **resultant**.

If the vectors are acting parallel to each other in the same direction, just add them together to find the resultant.

resultant = 7N to the left

If the vectors are acting parallel to each other in opposite directions, just subtract to find the resultant.

resultant = 1N to the right

If the vectors are acting at 90° to each other, the resultant can be found by drawing a scale diagram. Measure the angle to show the direction of the resultant force.

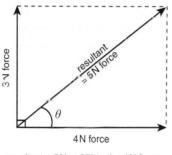

resultant = 5N at 37° to the 4N force

You can also find the resultant by calculation. Use:

$$v_R^2 = v_a^2 + v_b^2 \text{ and } \tan\theta = \frac{v_a}{v_b}$$

For example:

$$
\begin{aligned}
F_R^2 &= 3^2 + 4^2 \\
&= 9 + 16 \\
&= 25 \\
F_R &= 5\,N
\end{aligned}
$$

$$\tan\theta = \frac{3}{4} = 0.75$$
$$\theta = 37°$$

Equations of motion

You can use these equations in any situation where the acceleration is constant:

	where:
$s = \dfrac{(u + v)t}{2}$	s = distance
$v = u + at$	u = initial velocity
$v^2 = u^2 + 2as$	v = final velocity
	a = acceleration
$s = ut + \dfrac{1}{2}at^2$	t = time

Exam tip

You do not need to memorise these equations, but practise rearranging them and be sure that you know what the terms mean.

How science works

If you carry out practical work that involves finding the speed of an object, think carefully about the equipment that you are using, such as light gates, ticker tape timers or dataloggers.

The equipment used will determine the accuracy of your final answer.

Projectiles

Something that is thrown or fired is a **projectile**. Examples of projectiles are:

- balls
- darts
- missiles
- bullets
- cannon balls.

The path of a projectile is called its **trajectory**. An object that is projected horizontally in the Earth's gravitational field will follow a **parabolic** trajectory.

Horizontal and vertical

The horizontal and vertical velocities of a projectile are vectors. The resultant velocity of the projectile is the vector sum of the horizontal and vertical velocities.

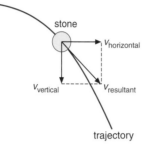

We can consider the horizontal and vertical motion separately.

If we ignore air resistance the projectile has:

Horizontally	Vertically
• no force • no acceleration • constant velocity	• gravitational force downwards only • acceleration downwards • increasing velocity downwards

The equations of uniformly accelerated motion can be applied to the horizontal and vertical motions separately.

Exam tip

In calculations involving projectiles it is useful to write down the information you have been given in the question, in terms of the symbols in the equations, separately for the horizontal and vertical motions.

Test yourself

1 Explain the difference between a scalar and a vector quantity. Give **three** examples of each.

2 A 6N force and a 7N force act on an object at right angles to each other. Determine the magnitude and direction of the resultant force on the object.

3 A car starts from rest and accelerates at a constant rate for 16 seconds to a speed of 30 m/s. Calculate the distance travelled during the acceleration.

4 A car accelerates from 10 m/s to 20 m/s with a constant acceleration of 0.5 m/s^2. Calculate the distance travelled during the acceleration.

5 A bullet is fired horizontally at a speed of 200 m/s and hits a target 100 m away. How far has the bullet fallen when it hits the target? Assume that the acceleration due to gravity is 10 m/s^2.

P5d Momentum

After revising this item you should:

● be able to state the opposite reactions to a number of actions, calculate momentum and relate it to force, explain what is meant by the conservation of momentum and use your ideas about momentum to explain some safety features in cars.

Action and reaction

When one object exerts a force on a second object there is always an equal and opposite force from the second object pushing on the first. Another way to say this is that every action has an equal and opposite reaction.

For example, if you push on a wall with a force of 3N to the right, the wall will push on you with a force of 3N to the left.

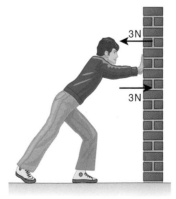

When you stand on the ground you apply a force vertically downwards on it – your weight. The ground pushes back on you with an equal upward force.

If two vehicles collide, each exerts equal and opposite forces on the other.

Momentum

The **momentum** of a body is given by the equation

$$\text{momentum} = \text{mass} \times \text{velocity}$$

- The greater the mass of a body, the greater its momentum.
- The greater the velocity of a body, the greater its momentum.

Since velocity is a vector quantity, momentum is also a vector. The direction of the momentum is the same as the direction of the velocity.

The unit of momentum is the kilogram metre per second (kg m/s) or newton second (Ns).

Momentum and force

Force and momentum are related by the equation

$$\text{force} = \frac{\text{change in momentum}}{\text{time}}$$

If an object is brought to a stop, its velocity is changed. And so its momentum is also changed.

- If the change in momentum happens over a short time, the force on the object will be large.
- If the change in momentum happens over a longer time, the force on the object will be smaller.

If the object is a human body, a bigger force means greater likelihood of serious injury.

Safety

If a car stops suddenly, e.g. in a collision, the passengers will still have momentum. They will suffer less injury if their momentum is changed slowly. This idea is used in a number of safety features in cars.

- Seat belts stretch slightly, increasing the time taken to stop, so reducing the force on the passenger.
- Air bags inflate, slowing the passenger over a longer time than it would take if the passenger hit the windscreen or other hard surfaces in the car.
- Crumple zones are designed to fold in a collision, increasing the time taken to come to a stop.

How science works

The technology is available to make cars safer than ever before, with features such as driver, passenger and side air bags, seat belts and crumple zones.

Who should pay for research into car safety? Should the best safety features be available on all cars or only on the most expensive models?

Conservation of momentum

The momentum before a collision is always equal to the momentum after the collision, so in any collision the total momentum of the system always stays the same. We call this the **conservation of momentum**. It relies on the fact that momentum is a vector – it has direction as well as size.

Exam tip

In calculations, decide on a positive direction (e.g. to the right is positive); any momentum in the opposite direction (e.g. to the left) will be negative.

Explosions

The conservation of momentum also applies to explosions.

- The total momentum before the explosion is zero.
- After the explosion the pieces go in all directions, but the total momentum of all the pieces added together will still be zero.

Recoil

Imagine a bullet in a gun. The total momentum of the bullet and the gun is zero. When the bullet is fired it is given a momentum in one direction; the gun moves in the opposite direction so the total momentum remains at zero.

The movement of the gun is known as the **recoil**.

The bullet has a small mass and a large velocity. The gun has a much larger mass, so its velocity is much less. In other words, the bullet moves quickly and the gun moves slowly.

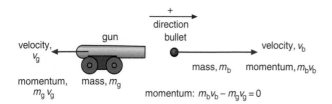

Rockets

Hot exhaust gases are pushed out of the back of a rocket. The rocket moves forward with an equal and opposite momentum.

Test yourself

1 What is the momentum of a 2000 kg car travelling at 25 m/s?

2 A lorry has a momentum of 100 000 kg m/s. Calculate the size of the braking force needed to stop the lorry in 6 s.

3 When gymnasts or athletes land after a jump they bend their knees or land on soft mats. Explain why this reduces the risk of injury.

4 In a laboratory experiment a trolley of mass 0.4 kg is moving at 2 m/s to the right. It hits a stationary trolley of mass 0.8 kg and they move off together. Calculate the velocity of the trolleys.

5 A gun of mass 0.5 kg fires a bullet of mass 0.01 kg. The speed of the bullet as it leaves the gun is 100 m/s. Calculate the recoil velocity of the gun.

P5e Satellite communication & P5f Nature of waves

After revising these items you should:

● be able to explain how microwaves and radio waves are used for communications and describe and explain the behaviour of waves.

Communicating

Mobile phones, TV and radio use electromagnetic waves to communicate through the atmosphere.

The waves used are:

● microwaves and radio waves
● at the lower frequency end of the electromagnetic spectrum.

The unit of frequency is the **hertz** (Hz). When referring to the electromagnetic spectrum we often use:

● **megahertz (MHz)**, one million hertz
● **gigahertz (GHz)**, one thousand million hertz.

Microwaves

Microwaves are:

● used to transmit information to orbiting satellites and retransmit back to Earth at a different frequency
● used because their higher frequencies pass through the ionosphere without reflection
● only diffracted by a small amount because of their short wavelength.

Radio waves

The uses of radio waves depend on their wavelengths and frequencies.

Radio waves with frequencies less than about 30 MHz (wavelengths greater than 10 m) are reflected by the ionosphere, so these cannot be used for satellite communication.

Diffraction

All waves can be diffracted. Diffraction is the spreading of waves as they move through a gap or around an object. Maximum diffraction occurs when the wavelength of the wave is equal to the size of the gap or object.

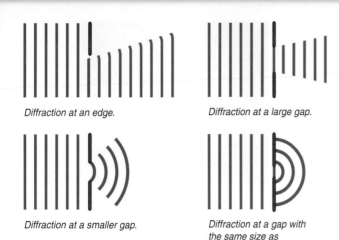

Diffraction at an edge.

Diffraction at a large gap.

Diffraction at a smaller gap.

Diffraction at a gap with the same size as the wavelength.

The diffraction of radio waves makes them suitable for broadcasting.

- Longer wavelength radio waves are diffracted around hills and over the horizon, so they can broadcast over a long range.
- Shorter wavelengths do not diffract as much, so cannot be detected over the horizon or on the other side of a hill. This effectively gives them a shorter range.

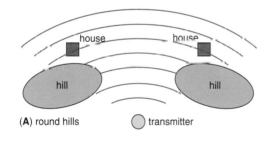

(A) round hills   ⬤ transmitter

short wave   long wave

(B) over hills

Exam tip

In the exam, if you are asked to draw a diagram to show diffraction make sure that you do this carefully, with a ruler.

Note that the wavelength does not change, so the distance between the lines should stay the same.

Amplitude modulation

Radio waves are not sound waves, so they cannot be heard. A sound wave can be added to a radio wave by a process called **amplitude modulation (AM)**.

The radio wave is called the carrier wave. The sound wave is changed into an electrical signal by a microphone and this signal is used to alter the amplitude of the radio wave. The opposite process takes place at a radio receiver and we hear the sound.

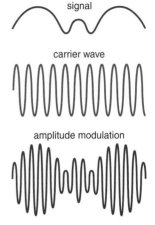

signal

carrier wave

amplitude modulation

Interference effects

When two waves overlap they produce **interference**. This effect can be demonstrated using:

- surface water waves on a ripple tank
- sound waves
- microwaves.

If the crests of two waves arrive at a point together and in phase, they reinforce to make a larger wave. This is called **constructive interference**.

When the trough of one wave arrives at a point with the crest of another wave they are out of phase. If the waves have the same amplitude they cancel each other completely. This is called **destructive interference**.

The result of these effects is an **interference pattern**.

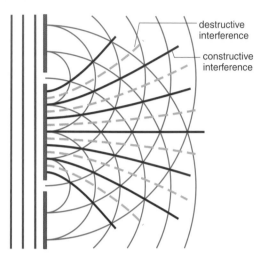

Path difference

The difference in the distances travelled by two waves, from the same source, to reach a particular point is called the **path difference**.

The following diagram shows that the waves travel different distances from the slits to reach point X.

- If the path difference is an even number of half wavelengths, constructive interference occurs.
- If it is an odd number of half wavelengths, destructive interference occurs.

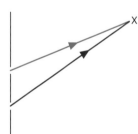

Diffraction of light

If you shine a light ray through two very small slits (gaps) that are very close together, you can form a pattern of light and dark areas on a screen. The light has to be in phase, so a laser light is often used. The pattern can only be explained if the light behaves as a wave.

If you use a diffraction grating, which consists of many slits per millimetre, you will see a brighter pattern of light and dark areas. This is called a **diffraction pattern**.

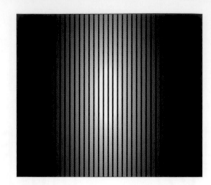

A diffraction pattern.

Polarisation

Electromagnetic waves are transverse waves – the directions of the vibrations of the wave are at 90° to the direction of travel of the wave.

Transverse waves can be **plane polarised**, meaning that the vibrations of the wave take place in one plane only (at 90° to the direction of travel of the wave).

The following diagram shows a wave passing through polarising filters that are lined up, but not through crossed polarising filters.

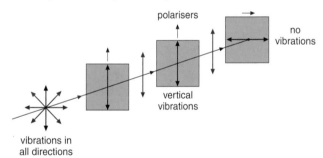

Visible light is usually unpolarised, but it is partially polarised when it reflects from a surface. The plastic in **Polaroid®** sunglasses only allows light vibrating in one plane through. It filters out the glare from a reflected surface, as the direction of the vibrations in this light is in the wrong plane.

How science works

For hundreds of years scientists have debated whether light is a particle or a wave. The model of light used by scientists today suggests that in some situations it behaves as a particle and in others as a wave. But new evidence in the future may cause them to modify their ideas.

P5g Refraction of waves

After revising this item you should:

● be able to explain what is meant by refraction, refractive index, dispersion and total internal reflection, and calculate the critical angle of a medium.

Refraction

When light waves cross the boundary from one **medium** to another there is a change in the:

• wave speed – this causes a change in the wavelength, but not the frequency

• direction of the waves, unless they are travelling along a **normal** – this effect is called refraction.

When a light ray moves from a less dense to a more dense medium (e.g. air to glass) the wave speed decreases and the light ray is refracted towards the normal.

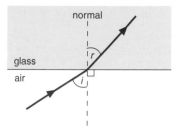

When a light ray moves from a more dense to a less dense medium (e.g. glass to air) the wave speed increases and the light ray is refracted away from the normal.

The **refractive index** of a medium is given by this formula:

$$\text{refractive index} = \frac{\text{speed of light in a vacuum}}{\text{speed of light in the medium}}$$

The speed of light in a vacuum is 300 000 000 m/s, but it travels more slowly in a medium.

The bigger the refractive index of a medium, the bigger the change in speed and the bigger the change in direction of the light.

Snell's law

The refractive index of a medium can also be expressed in terms of angles, using **Snell's law**.

$$n = \frac{\sin i}{\sin r}$$

where n = refractive index
i = angle of incidence
r = angle of refraction

The angles are always measured between the light ray and the normal. For example:

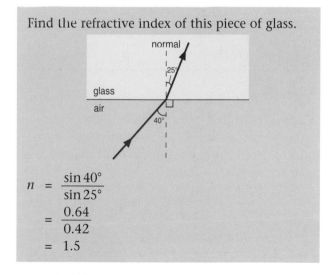

Find the refractive index of this piece of glass.

$$n = \frac{\sin 40°}{\sin 25°}$$
$$= \frac{0.64}{0.42}$$
$$= 1.5$$

Exam tip

Refractive index is a ratio, so it has no units.

Dispersion

Different colours of light travel at slightly different speeds in a medium and so are refracted by slightly different amounts.

You can see this if you shine a ray of white light onto a triangular glass prism, because a spectrum is produced.

This is called **dispersion**.

Colours at the blue end of the spectrum are refracted the most. Those at the red end are refracted the least.

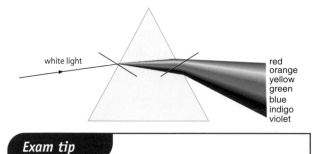

Exam tip

You need to know the order of the colours in the spectrum, and that the blue end of the spectrum is refracted most. Use this phrase or another to help you remember:

*'**r**inse **o**ut **y**our **g**reasy **b**ottles **i**n **v**inegar' for 'red, orange, yellow, green, blue, indigo, violet'*

and

*'**b**lues **b**end **b**est'.*

Critical angle

When a ray of light travels from a medium with a higher refractive index to a medium with a lower refractive index (e.g. glass to air) it is refracted away from the normal.

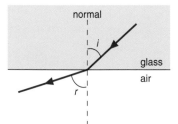

i is less than critical angle

As the angle of incidence increases, the angle of refraction increases until the ray is refracted along the boundary between the surfaces. When this happens the angle of incidence is equal to the critical angle.

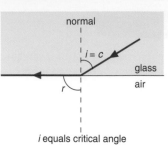

i equals critical angle

If the angle of incidence is greater than the critical angle, the ray of light does not escape from the medium – total internal reflection takes place.

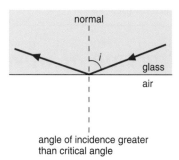

angle of incidence greater than critical angle

Different media have different critical angles. The higher the refractive index of a medium, the lower its critical angle. This helps to explain why diamonds sparkle so much.

The critical angle for a boundary between two media can be calculated using

$$\sin c = \frac{n_r}{n_i}$$

where c = critical angle

n_r = refractive index of refracting medium

n_i = refractive index of incident medium

How science works

You can carry out a practical investigation yourself to determine the refractive index or critical angle of glass.

It is important to use a narrow ray, mark the positions of the rays and glass with a sharp pencil, and measure angles very carefully if you want your results to be accurate.

1 What is a normal?

2 The speed of light in air is 300 000 000 m/s. Calculate the speed of light in water if the refractive index of water is 1.5.

3 Explain why total internal reflection can occur when light travels from glass into air but not from air into glass.

4 A ray of light has an angle of incidence of 24° as it enters some water. The angle of refraction in the water is 18°. Calculate the refractive index of water.

5 Explain why dispersion occurs when white light travels thorough a triangular glass prism, but not when it travels through opposite sides of a rectangular glass block.

P5h Optics

After revising this item you should:

- be able to describe the effect of a converging lens on light, explain the difference between a real and a virtual image and describe how convex lenses are used in magnifying glasses, cameras and projectors.

Convex lenses

Parallel rays of light that pass through a **convex lens** are refracted so that they converge to a point called the **focal point**, F. The distance from the centre of the lens to the focal point is the **focal length**, f.

The following diagram shows that the thicker the lens at its centre, the shorter its focal length.

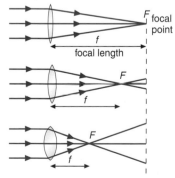

A convex lens makes diverging rays converge.

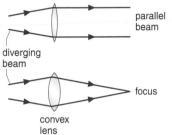

You can find the position and size of the **image** formed by a convex lens by drawing a ray diagram.

- The principal axis is the line through the centre of the lens and at right angles to it. Include this in your diagram.
- Mark the focal point with an F. There is a focal point on each side of the lens.

Use three 'construction' rays in your diagram. They come from a single point on the object and help to locate the corresponding point on the image.

- The ray through the centre of the lens passes straight on without refraction.
- The ray parallel to the principal axis is refracted through the focal point.
- The ray through the focal point is refracted parallel to the principal axis.

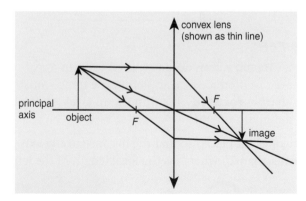

Exam tip

You may need to draw a ray diagram in the exam. You must keep the lines neat and use a sharp pencil – if you don't, the image will not be in the correct place.

You only need two rays to locate the position of the image, but drawing the third construction ray will check that the position you have found is correct.

Real and virtual

A **real image** is one that can be formed on a screen because rays of light actually pass through it. It is **inverted** (upside down).

A **virtual image** is one that cannot be formed on a screen because the rays of light only appear to pass through it. It is upright (the right way up).

Magnifying glass

If an object is placed very close to a convex lens (between the focal point and the lens) a virtual, upright, magnified image is produced.

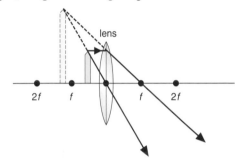

Magnification

The **magnification** produced can be calculated using the formula

$$\text{magnification} = \frac{\text{image height}}{\text{object height}}$$

Camera

In a camera, a convex lens is used to form a real image. To produce a clear picture the image must be sharply **focused** on a film (or an array of pixels in a digital camera).

The object is placed so that the distance to the lens is greater than 2*f*, where *f* is the focal length of the lens.

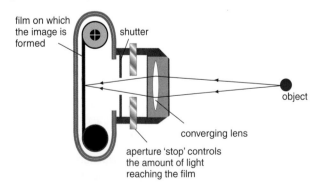

film on which the image is formed

shutter

object

converging lens

aperture 'stop' controls the amount of light reaching the film

Projector

In a projector the object is positioned so that the distance to the lens is between *f* and 2*f* (where *f* is the focal length). The image produced is real, inverted and magnified.

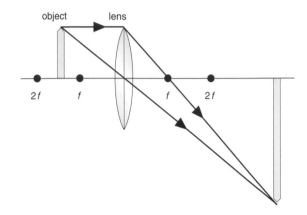

How science works

The improvements in digital camera technology mean that we are regularly photographed or recorded when going about our daily lives, and without our knowledge or consent.

Is this reasonable? Who monitors how much we are monitored?

Test yourself

1 How does the focal length of a convex lens change as the shape of the lens changes?

2 An object is placed 6 cm from a convex lens. The focal length of the lens is 4 cm. Use a ray diagram to find the position of the image.

3 Where must an object be placed, relative to a convex lens, to produce an image that is exactly the same size as the object?

4 A convex lens produces a magnification of 5. How high will the image of a 1.5 cm tall object be?

5 Why does the image in a digital camera need to be real?

P6a Resisting & P6b Sharing

Changing resistance

A variable resistor contains a length of **resistance wire**. Varying the length of this wire changes the resistance.

Variable resistors are used as controls in circuits. Increasing the resistance decreases the current in the circuit. This can be used to dim a bulb or slow a motor.

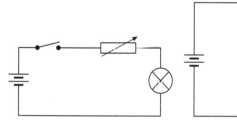 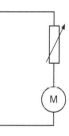

When the resistance is increased the bulb gets dimmer.

When the resistance is increased the motor slows down.

Calculating resistance

You can calculate resistance using the formula

$$\text{resistance} = \frac{\text{voltage}}{\text{current}} \qquad \text{or} \qquad R = \frac{V}{I}$$

The unit of resistance is the ohm (Ω).

Exam tip

For some more demanding exam questions, you will have to rearrange this equation.

$$V = RI \qquad\qquad I = \frac{V}{R}$$

Components such as resistors and metallic conductors, like wires, are called **ohmic devices** or **ohmic conductors**. The resistance of these components is constant, provided their temperature stays constant.

● A graph of the voltage against current for an ohmic conductor is a straight line through the origin.

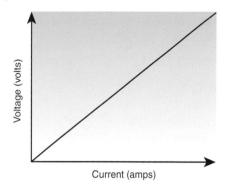

For a **non-ohmic device** or **non-ohmic conductor**, the resistance changes as the voltage or current changes.

● The voltage–current graph for a non-ohmic conductor is not a straight line.

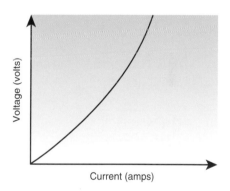

A filament lamp produces a graph like the one above. As the current through the filament increases:

● the temperature of the filament increases
● its resistance increases
● so the line curves.

Exam tip

Take care with voltage–current graphs. Sometimes the voltage and current axes are switched around.

Potential divider

Voltage can also be called potential difference (p.d.). Two fixed resistors can be used as a **potential divider** as shown in the diagram.

The two resistors are in series, so the same current flows through each of them.

If $R_1 = R_2$, then $V_1 = V_2$.

If the value of R_1 is twice that of R_2, then V_1 will be double V_2. The potential differences across the resistors are divided in the same proportion as the resistances.

The output p.d., V_{out} can be found using the formula

$$V_{out} = V_{in} \times \frac{R_2}{(R_1 + R_2)}$$

For example:

If the input p.d. is 12 V, R_1 is 2000 Ω and R_2 is 500 Ω, find the output p.d.

$$V_{out} = 12 \times \frac{500}{(2000 + 500)}$$
$$= 12 \times 0.2$$
$$= 2.4 \text{ V}$$

If the potential divider has one fixed resistor and one variable resistor, the output p.d., V_{out}, can be varied.

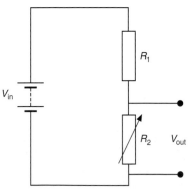

Light-dependent resistor (LDR)

The resistance of a **light-dependent resistor (LDR)** decreases as the light intensity falling on it increases.

An LDR can be used in a potential divider circuit to provide an output that depends on the light conditions.

For example, an LDR can be used to switch on a lighting circuit when it gets dark.

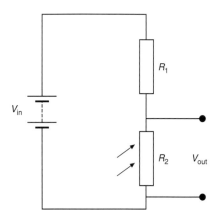

As the light intensity decreases, the resistance of R_2 increases and the output potential difference, V_{out}, increases.

The value of V_{out} that is just enough to switch on the lighting circuit is called the **threshold** p.d. If R_1 is a variable resistor it can be altered to change the value of the threshold p.d.

Thermistor

The resistance of a **thermistor** decreases as the temperature increases.

A thermistor can be used in a potential divider circuit to provide an output that depends on the temperature of the surroundings.

For example, a thermistor can be used to switch on a heating circuit when it gets cold.

How science works

The development of automatic switching circuits means that humans do not need to be around to do the job.

Is this a good thing or a bad thing?

P6c Motoring

After revising this item you should:

- be able to explain how the forces on a current-carrying coil in a magnetic field produce a turning effect and describe how this is used in an electric motor.

Current and magnetic fields

When an electric current passes through a conductor a magnetic field is produced around the conductor.

Different conductors produce different shaped fields. The direction of the field lines is always shown from north to south.

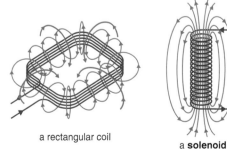

a rectangular coil

a **solenoid**

Fleming's left-hand rule

If a wire carrying a current is placed in a magnetic field it may experience a force. The force is a maximum if the wire is at right angles to the magnetic field.

Fleming's left-hand rule can be used to work out the direction of the force.

- The first finger represents the direction of the magnetic field (north to south).
- The second finger represents the direction of the current (positive to negative).
- The thumb gives the direction of the force, and the direction in which the wire will move if it is not fixed in position.

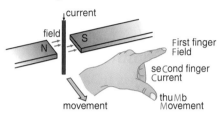

Reversing the current or reversing the field reverses the direction of the force.

The DC motor

In a simple **DC motor** a coil is placed between the poles of a magnet. The coil is on an axle so it is free to turn. When a current flows through the coil it experiences a force.

Fleming's left-hand rule shows that one side of the coil experiences an upward force and the other side experiences a downward force. This produces a turning effect and the coil rotates.

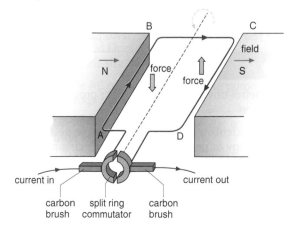

P6e Transforming

After revising this item you should:

- be able to describe the construction of a transformer, explain how it changes the size of an alternating voltage and explain why power is transmitted at high voltages.

The transformer

A **transformer** is used to change the size of an AC voltage.

A transformer consists of two coils of insulated wire wound onto the same iron core.

1. An alternating current is passed through the **primary coil**.
2. This produces a changing magnetic field in the core.
3. The changing magnetic field passes through the **secondary coil**.
4. This causes an alternating voltage across the ends of the coil.
5. If there is a complete circuit, a current flows through the secondary coil.

The current has to be AC. If DC were used the magnetic field would not continually change and no voltage would be induced.

- In a **step-up transformer** there are more turns in the secondary coil than in the primary coil, so the voltage produced across the secondary coil is greater – stepped up.

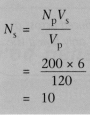

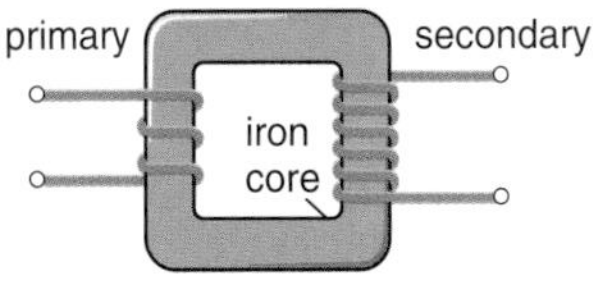

step-up transformer

- In a **step-down transformer** there are more turns in the primary coil than in the secondary coil, so the voltage induced across the secondary coil is less – stepped down.

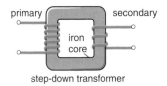

step-down transformer

The voltage induced by the transformer can be calculated using the following equation.

$$\frac{V_p}{V_s} = \frac{N_p}{N_s}$$

where V_p = voltage across the primary coil
V_s = voltage across the secondary coil
N_p = number of turns on the primary coil
N_s = number of turns on the secondary coil

For example:

A transformer changes an input voltage of 120 V to an output of 6 V. There are 200 turns on the primary coil. How many turns are there on the secondary coil?

$$N_s = \frac{N_p V_s}{V_p}$$

$$= \frac{200 \times 6}{120}$$

$$= 10$$

Exam tip

In exam questions using the transformer equation, check that your answer is sensible. For example, if you are dealing with a step-up transformer check that the secondary voltage is bigger than the primary voltage.

Isolating transformer

An **isolating transformer**:

- has equal numbers of turns on the primary and secondary coils
- does not change the value of the voltage
- is used in some mains circuits for safety reasons (e.g. a bathroom shaver socket)
- has no electrical link between the two sets of coils
- has less risk of contacts between live parts and the earth wire.

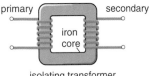

isolating transformer

Transmission of electricity

When electricity is transmitted across the power lines of the National Grid, some energy is lost due to the resistance of the cables.

The rate at which energy is lost (power loss) in the cables is given by the following formula.

$$P = I^2R$$

where P = power loss
I = current in the cables
R = resistance of the cables

So reducing the current reduces the power loss. Reducing the current by a factor of two reduces the power loss by a factor of four.

Power can also be found using this formula.

$$P = IV$$

where P = power transmitted
I = current in the cables
V = voltage transmitted

So to transmit a given power at a reduced current, we must increase the voltage.

- At power stations step-up transformers are used to increase the voltage for transmission.
- At sub-stations the voltage is reduced before the power is supplied to consumers.

Transformer efficiency

Transformers are very efficient, so we assume that the input power is equal to the output power.

$$I_pV_p = I_sV_s$$

where I_p = current in the primary
I_s = current in the secondary

So if the current in the primary is reduced, the primary voltage is increased.

How science works

Some people believe that living underneath overhead power cables is dangerous because of the magnetic field produced around the lines.

A link between overhead power lines and illness has not been proved. So at present builders are allowed to build houses near power lines.

Test yourself

1. Draw a labelled diagram of a simple step-up transformer.
2. Explain why the coils of a transformer are made from insulated wire.
3. In a transformer there is a voltage of 3 V across a primary coil of 12 turns. There are 48 turns on the secondary coil which is connected across a lamp. Calculate the voltage across the lamp.
4. Explain why a transformer does not work with a direct current.
5. A transformer has a primary coil with 25 turns and a secondary coil with 250 turns. A lamp marked 120 V, 60 W is connected across the secondary coil. Calculate:

   (a) the voltage across the primary coil
   (b) the current in the lamp.

P6f Charging

After revising this item you should:

- be able to describe how a single diode can produce half-wave rectification, how four diodes can produce full-wave rectification and explain how a capacitor is used in a simple smoothing circuit.

The diode

The following graph shows how the current varies with voltage for a **diode**.

- In the forward direction, as the voltage increases the current increases.
- When the supply is reversed the resistance of the diode is extremely high, so no current flows.

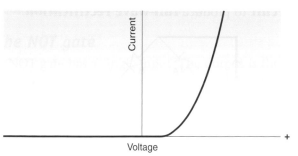

The AND gate

The output of an **AND gate** is high when both input A and input B are high.

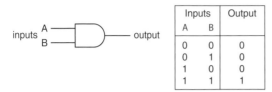

Inputs		Output
A	B	
0	0	0
0	1	0
1	0	0
1	1	1

The OR gate

The output of an **OR gate** is high when either input A or input B is high, or when both inputs are high.

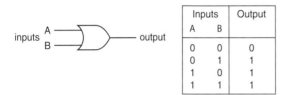

Inputs		Output
A	B	
0	0	0
0	1	1
1	0	1
1	1	1

The NAND gate

A **NAND gate** produces the same output as an AND gate followed by a NOT gate.

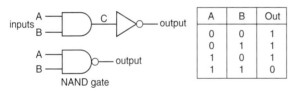

A	B	Out
0	0	1
0	1	1
1	0	1
1	1	0

The NOR gate

A **NOR gate** produces the same output as an OR gate followed by a NOT gate.

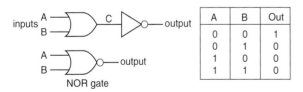

A	B	Out
0	0	1
0	1	0
1	0	0
1	1	0

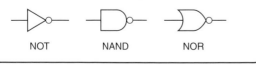
Providing inputs

Potential divider circuits (see page 60) can be used to provide inputs for logic gates.

A potential divider circuit with a thermistor can provide an input signal that depends on temperature (see also page 60).

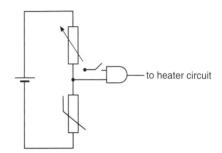

A heater control circuit.

A potential divider circuit with a LDR can provide an input signal that depends on light intensity (see also page 60).

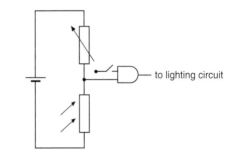

A lighting control circuit.

The circuits shown include a variable resistor, so the temperature or light intensity at which the input to the AND gate goes high can be adjusted.

The bistable latch circuit

We can use two NOR gates to make a circuit called a **bistable latch**.

- A brief high signal at one input makes the output go high.
- The output stays high until there is a high signal at the other input.
- Low signals at both inputs leave the output unchanged.

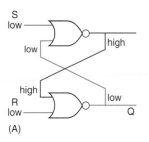

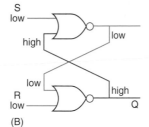

(A)

(B)

SR latch starting conditions.

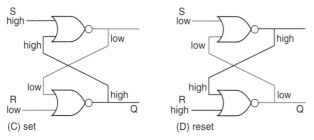

(C) set

(D) reset

When S is high and when R is high.

The light-emitting diode (LED)

A **light-emitting diode (LED)** is a diode that emits light when current flows through it, so it can be used to indicate that the output for a logic gate is high.

A high current will break an LED, so a resistor is placed in series with it in a circuit to limit the current.

The relay

A **relay**:

- uses a small current in one circuit to switch on a large current in another circuit
- allows a 5 V output from a logic gate to switch on a device, like a heater or motor, in a mains circuit
- isolates the logic gate circuit from the mains.

A relay consists of a small coil next to an iron switch.

- When current flows the coil acts as an electromagnet, closing the switch.
- When the current stops a spring opens the switch.

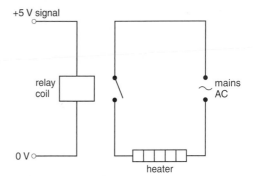

A relay used to switch on a heater.

Test yourself

1 Draw the symbol and give the truth table for a NAND gate.

2 Write down the truth table for this logic circuit.

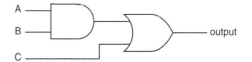

3 Which logic gate has the following truth table?

Input A	Input B	Output
0	0	1
0	1	0
1	0	0
1	1	0

4 Explain why relays are used.

5 An electronic system is designed to set off an alarm if either one or both of two pressure sensors are activated. There is also a switch to turn the system on and off. Draw:

(a) a truth table for the system
(b) a circuit of logic gates to switch the alarm on.

Exam-style questions

1 Samir and Mena are going on a picni. They plan to take some cold bottles of drink with them.

(a) Samir and Mena make a box to keep the bottles of drink cold. They make the box from expanded polystyrene covered in a layer of aluminium foil. The polystyrene contains many tiny air bubbles.

(i) Suggest why they made the box from expanded polystyrene.

....

....

....[3]

(ii) Suggest why they covered the box in aluminium foil.

....[1]

(b) They put 'freezer packs' into the box to help keep the bottles of drink cold. A freezer pack is a thick polythene bag containing a liquid. If the liquid is left in a freezer at −20°C overnight it turns into a solid.

(i) Explain how the freezer packs help to keep the bottles of drink cold.

....

....[2]

(ii) The table gives some information about three liquids.

Liquid	Melting point (°C)	Specific latent heat of fusion (J/kg)
ethanol	−114	109 000
salt water	−12	333 000
cyclohexane	7	39 000

Why is salt water used, rather than the other liquids, in the freezer packs?

Use the table to help you.

....

....[2]

2 (a) (i) Describe how electricity is generated at a coal-fired power station.

....

....

....

....[3]

(ii) Electricity from a power station is transmitted across the country using the National Grid. Explain why transformers are used to increase the voltage before transmission.

....

....

....[3]

(b) A hairdryer is connected to the 230 V mains supply. It uses a current of 6 A.

(i) Calculate the power of the hairdryer in kilowatts. Use the equation.

power = voltage × current

[2]

(ii) The hairdryer is used for 15 minutes. Calculate the cost of the electrical energy supplied if 1 kWh costs 9p.

[2]

3 At a skydiving club, Sonia is flying an aircraft with a take-off speed of 32 m/s.

The aircraft accelerates from 0 to 32 m/s in 8 s.

(a) Calculate the acceleration of the aircraft.

....

....

....[2]

(b) In the air, the aircraft accelerates at 2.5 m/s^2 from a speed of 32 m/s to its cruising speed of 82 m/s. Calculate the time to reach cruising speed.

....

....

....[2]

(c) The aircraft has a mass of 3800 kg. Calculate the kinetic energy it has at cruising speed.

....

....

....[2]

Jim begins his skydive from the aircraft.

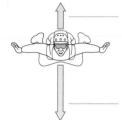

(d) Label the two forces on Jim as he starts falling. [2]

(e) After a few seconds Jim reaches a steady speed. Why does he reach a steady speed?

....[1]

4 In hospitals, ultrasound is used for scanning parts of the body.

(a) Give **two** reasons why ultrasound is used, and not X-rays, to scan the fetus in the womb.

....

....[2]

(b) How is ultrasound different to normal sound?

....

....[2]

(c) Ultrasound is a longitudinal wave. This diagram shows a longitudinal wave in a spring.

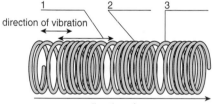

direction of vibration

direction of wave

(i) Complete the **three** labels on the diagram. [3]

(ii) Describe how the air particles move when a longitudinal ultrasound wave travels through the air.

....

....[2]

5 Some scientists are using remotely controlled cars to investigate collisions in a crash test laboratory.

(a) The scientists crash a car of mass 1500 kg travelling at 20 m/s into a stationary car of mass 2000 kg.

(i) Calculate the momentum of the moving car. Include a unit with your answer.

[3]

(ii) After the collision the two cars move off together. Calculate the velocity of the cars after the collision.

[3]

(b) The cars in the test are fitted with seat belts and air bags.

Explain how a seat belt and air bag help to reduce injuries to a passenger in a collision.

....

....

....

....

....[4]

6 Fiona is investigating electricity and motion. She makes a circuit using a cell, a switch and a piece of flexible wire. She suspends the wire vertically so that it hangs freely between the poles of a horseshoe-shaped magnet.

(a) Explain why the wire moves when the switch is closed.

....

....

....[3]

(b) State and explain what would happen if she:

(i) reversed the connections to the cell

....

....[2]

(ii) replaced the magnet with a more powerful one

....

....[2]

(iii) replaced the cell with a battery.

....

....

....[3]

Answers to exam-style questions

1 (a) (i) Expanded polystyrene contains many trapped air bubbles; Air is a poor conductor; So the contents stay cool [3]

(ii) Aluminium foil reflects infrared [1]

(b) (i) Heat energy flows from the box to the freezer packs; The energy is used to melt the freezer packs [2]

(ii) The freezer is not cold enough to freeze ethanol; Salt water has a higher specific latent heat than cyclohexane so more energy is taken from the surroundings to melt it [2]

2 (a) (i) Coal is burned to produce heat which heats water; The water turns to steam which drives a turbine; The turbine drives a generator, producing electricity [3]

(ii) Increasing the voltage decreases the current; Lower current means less heating of the cables; This reduces wastage of energy [3]

(b) (i) Power = 6A × 230V; Power = 1380W = 1.38 kW [2]

(ii) Electrical energy = 1.38 kW × 0.25 hours = 0.345 kWh; Cost = 0.345 × 9p = 3.1p [2]

3 (a) Acceleration = change in velocity/time (or a = v/t) = 32/8; 4 m/s^2 [2]

(b) Time = change in velocity/acceleration (or t = v/a) = 50/2.5; 20 s [2]

(c) 0.5 × 3800 × (82)^2; 12 800 000 / 12 775 600 J [2]

(d) Upwards force: drag; Downwards force: weight [2]

(e) Drag = weight / drag increases [1]

4 (a) Can image soft tissues; Does not damage soft tissue / X-rays do damage soft tissue [2]

(b) Higher frequency; Above threshold of human hearing [2]

(c) (i) Left to right: Wavelength; Compression; Rarefaction [3]

(ii) Back and forth / oscillate; In / parallel to direction of travel [2]

5 (a) (i) Momentum = 1500 kg × 20 m/s; Momentum = 30 000; kg m/s or Ns [3]

(ii) Total mass = 1500 + 2000 = 3500 kg; Momentum before = momentum after / 30 000 = 3500v; v = 30 000/3500 = 8.6 m/s [3]

(b) Seat belt stops the passenger's forward movement; In doing this it stretches slightly, increasing the time to stop the passenger; Air bag inflates and slows the passenger over a longer time than if they were to hit the dashboard; Increasing the time to stop the passenger decreases the force on them [4]

6 (a) There is a current in the wire when switch is closed; A current carrying conductor in a magnetic field experiences a force; The force on the wire causes it to move [3]

(b) (i) Wire would move in the opposite direction; Because the directions of the current and force are reversed [2]

(ii) Wire would move faster / more; Because the force on the wire would be greater [2]

(iii) Wire would move faster / more; Because the potential difference across the wire would be greater; So the current in the wire would be greater [3]

Index of key words

Answers to test yourself questions

P1a

1 3 kg × 10°C × 4200 J/kg/°C = 126 000 J or 126 kJ **2** (88 000 J/2 kg)/100°C = 440 J/kg/°C **3** Ice at 0°C takes in heat from your drink to become water at 0°C **4** (9900 J/330 000 J/kg) = 0.03 kg **5** As well as the burn, heat from steam condensing to water (specific latent heat) is absorbed by the skin

P1b & P1c

1 Stone conducts heat away from your feet better than carpet **2** Cavity wall insulation **3** It is a good insulator and reduces heat convection from tank to room **4** (92/100) × 100% = 92% **5** (a) 48 J (b) Transferred to kinetic energy to move the fan blades **6** A single wall conducts heat energy well; the air space between two walls is a good insulator **7** They prevent air movement, which would lose heat by convection **8** White reflects radiant energy from the Sun; black absorbs heat energy

P1d & P1e

1 Microwaves cause currents to flow in metals, which may heat the metal enough to cause a fire **2** Analogue signals can be of any value; digital signals are either on or off **3** It leaves the glass and goes into the air **4** Visible light, infrared **5** Light travels faster than anything else

P1f

1 They change speed and this makes them change direction **2** Thieves could break into the network and steal information **3** To reflect communications transmissions, they do not move **4** Less noise interference, giving a better quality signal; many more signals can be broadcast from the same aerial **5** When the size of the gap is similar to the wavelength

P1g

1 Number of waves per second **2** 19 Hz × 10 mm = 190 mm/s or 0.19 m/s **3** 96 m/s / 0.08 m = 1200 Hz **4** More secure: it prevents other people from knowing what is being transmitted **5** Light has a higher frequency so can carry more information per second

P1h

1 P-waves travel faster and can travel through liquids **2** More ultraviolet radiation reaches the Earth's surface, which is likely to increase the incidence of cancer **3** 3 hours **4** Climate change could mean some plants do not have the level of sunlight they need and become extinct; this disrupts the food supply of some animals so they also become extinct **5** (a) −0.05°C (b) + 0.42°C (c) Up until about 1920 the average global temperature change was relatively small. From 1920 to 1950 it rose steeply and has stayed at high levels since (d) E.g. dust from volcanoes / forest fires has released a lot of carbon dioxide into the atmosphere (e) E.g. an increasing population has led to more burning of fossil fuels

P2a

1 It will not run out **2** Light to electrical energy **3** (a) E.g. cover up parts of the photocell with cardboard pieces (b) Repeat the experiment several times until she gets consistent results (c) Light source intensity **4** The amount of power from each turbine is limited by the wind speed and the mechanical ability of the turbine **5** More wind, less visual / noise pollution

P2b

1 Increases **2** 300 J/1000 J = 0.3 **3** 100 J/0.5 = 200 J **4** Less expensive **5** Less energy is wasted heating the wires

P2c

1 Currently a reliable source of energy, not dependent on weather or time of day, can start up gas power stations immediately if sudden power demand **2** 1800 W/230 V = 7.8 A **3** (2300 W × 1.5 h)/1000 = 3.45 kWh × 7 p = 24 p **4** 1.5 kW × (6/60 h) = 0.15 kWh × 10 p = 1.5 p **5** Heat given out by the nuclear reaction of uranium with neutrons is used to boil water and produce steam under pressure. This steam turns the blades of a turbine connected to a generator, which transfers kinetic energy into electrical energy

P2d

1 Alpha particles are stopped by a few centimetres of air **2** Alpha is absorbed by paper; gamma passes through paper **3** Knocking electrons off atoms, turning them into charged particles (ions) **4** They are the most penetrating and can cause ionisation in living cells, resulting in cell death or cancer **5** It causes the most ionisation in cells, resulting in cell death or cancer

P2e & P2f

1 Magnetic field lines as in lower diagram on page 20 **2** The result of a collision between Earth and a large planet billions of years ago; there are other equally sensible theories **3** Any three from: telecommunications, spying, navigation, monitoring weather **4** They reflect light from the Sun **5** No need to provide the essentials for life on board e.g. food, water, warmth, oxygen

P2g & P2h

1 Asteroids are large rocks; comets are balls of ice and dust **2** Impact craters on Earth, layers of unusual elements in rocks, a sudden drop in the number of living creatures **3** The Universe is still filled with microwave radiation **4** It doesn't emit light **5** Cloud of gas and dust pulled together by gravity, fusion reactions begin giving a main sequence star, runs out of hydrogen fuel and becomes a red giant, turns into a supernova which explodes and throws its outer layer into space, the dense core remains as a neutron star, becomes a black hole if mass is large enough

P3a

1 10.24 m/s **2** 12.5 s **3** (a) 25 + 160 = 185 m (b) Graph with time on x-axis and speed y-axis; horizontal line at 50 km/h from time 0h to 1/2h; vertical line upwards from 50 km/h to 80 km/h; horizontal line from 1/2h to 2h at 80 km/h **4** (a) Ivan (b) Shirley (c) Chris – 10 m/s; Joy – 5 m/s

P3b

1 (a) 4 m/s (b) 80 s (c) B (d) 120 m (e) 0.4 m/s² **2** Graph with time on x-axis and speed on y-axis; A – straight line rising from origin to coordinate (5 s, 20 m/s); B – horizontal straight line to 15 s at 20 m/s height; C – straight line rising to coordinate (20 s, 50 m/s); D – straight line sloping downwards to meet x-axis at 40 s **3** 90 m/s **4** C, D

P3c & P3d

1 (a) 7000 N (b) 2 m/s² **2** Boat is pushed backwards with a force equal and opposite to the force which the rower pushes onto the bank **3** (a) 6 m at 20 mph, 12 m at 40 mph (b) 6 m at 20 mph and 24 m at 40 mph **4** (a) 96 J (b) 12 N **5** (a) 60 m (b) 640 W (c) 60 s **6** (a) (i) The more power, the more carbon dioxide emitted (ii) Fuel consumption increases as power increases (b) (i) £12.78 (ii) £4.32

P3e & P3f

1 (a) A (b) B **2** 1200 × (26)² = 811 200 J **3** 96 m **4** Battery-powered cars do not pollute when they are driven, but the energy needed to charge them is produced by power stations which cause pollution **5** (a) Increases collision time and distance; driver decelerated more slowly (b) Crumple zones or air bags

P3g

1 (a) No speed, no drag force (b) Increasing speed, increasing drag force (c) Constant speed, constant drag force **2** A – arrow labelled weight pointing downwards, smaller arrow labelled drag pointing upwards, the parachutist is accelerating; B – as A, but drag arrow is now the same size as weight arrow, the parachutist has reached terminal velocity; C – drag arrow is now bigger than weight arrow, the parachute has increased the drag force, slowing the parachutist down; D – drag arrow is still bigger than the weight arrow, but not by as much, speed reduces until new terminal speed is reached **3** A, C, D, E **4** B **5** When the parachute is opened, the drag force is greatly increased and the car's speed rapidly decreases

P3h

1 B, C **2** 10 kg mass 6 m above the Earth **3** (a) PE = 2000 × 10 × 20 = 400 000 N (b) Decreases (c) KE gained = PE lost = 400 000 N; KE = 400 000 = 1/2 × 2000 × v²; v² = 400; v = 20 m/s **4** (a) Four times, or 3 600 000 J (b) Car B has twice as much mass as car A **5** (a) 600 N (b) 0.1 kg

P4a

1 (a) They lose electrons (b) They gain electrons **2** (a) It is repelled (b) They have opposite charges **3** Powders in the air burn very quickly if a spark occurs **4** Earthing prevents sparks from occurring **5** (a) The surface of the monitor is charged (b) Anti-static sprays, liquids and cloths reduce the build-up of charge

P4b

1 (a) To improve conduction of electricity (b) So that no bystanders get a shock (c) The heart is made to contract **2** (a) Heat causes the particles to rise up (b) Electrons

3 (a) Positive or negative, depending on the design (b) The particles clump together and are heavy enough to fall **4** (a) The paint particles are attracted to the car body (b) All of the paint is attracted to the car (c) Parts underneath the car body also get painted **5** A, E

P4c

1 (a) Decreases (b) Decreases 2 600 ohms **3** (a) 240 V (b) 0.03 A **4** (a) When too much current flows, the fuse melts, breaking the circuit (b) (i) 13 A (ii) 13 A (iii) 3 A **5** (a) Reacts quicker; it doesn't have to be replaced, only reset (b) It has a non-conducting case (c) To stop the case from carrying current and becoming live

P4d & P4e

1 (a) (i) At right angles to the direction of travel of the wave (ii) Parallel to the direction of travel of the wave (b) The particles move a greater distance (c) The distance between wave repeats (two compressions or two rarefactions) **2** Ultrasound beam sent into the body. Each time it crosses a boundary between tissues some of it is reflected. A computer converts these reflections into a picture **3** They are both electromagnetic waves; gamma rays come from nuclear radiation, X-rays from stopping fast moving electrons **4** A, D, E, G **5** (a) A wide gamma ray beam is rotated round the patient, keeping the tumour at the centre so it receives a concentrated dose of gamma rays; the non-cancerous tissue gets only a weak dose (b) Lead-lined apron; badges which measure the radiation dose, so they know when their limit is reached

P4f

1 (a) The average time for half of a sample of radioactive nuclei to decay (b) A particle made up of 2 protons and 2 neutrons (c) A very fast moving electron **2** (a) one million atoms (b) 12 hours (c) 1/16 **3** (a) Column 1: (1000), 700, (500), 300; column 2: 0, (10) 18, (25) (b) 18 hours **4** (a) Decrease (b) $^{238}U \longrightarrow {}^{4}\alpha + {}^{234}Th$ **5** (a) Protons increase, neutrons decrease (b) $^{12}B \longrightarrow {}^{0}\beta + {}^{12}C$

P4g & P4h

1 (a) (i) 12% (ii) 12% (b) Depends on content of rocks and soil, sites of nuclear power plants, position of the Sun **2** (a) carbon-14 (b) (i) Diffusion (ii) Respiration (c) When organism dies, exchange of carbon dioxide with atmosphere stops. Activity of C-14 measured today and amount of activity in sample shows how long ago the organism died (d) The amount of C-14 in the atmosphere **3** X – 5500 years; Y – 11000 years; Z – 0 years (modern) **4** (a) Splitting of the nucleus of an atom (b) A reaction which continues and grows faster because of the products formed from each reaction (c) Device in which chain reactions are controlled to produce heat (d) Material used to absorb excess neutrons from a nuclear reaction and prevent it from running out of control **5** (a) Uranium (b) A source of neutrons

(c) More than one neutron is given out from one reaction (d) By using control rods which absorb excess neutrons

P5a

1 (a) Gravity (b) Towards the Earth (c) It would move away in a straight line at a tangent to the circle **2** Above the equator; period of 24 hours; height of 35800 km; above fixed position on Earth **3** (a) A (b) B (c) A **4** Weather forecasting, monitoring climate change, spying **5** The comet reaches its maximum speed as it passes around the Sun because the gravitational force is at its maximum and then slows down as it moves away from the Sun because the force decreases

P5b & P5c

1 Scalars have magnitude only; vectors have both magnitude and direction. Scalars: distance, speed, energy; vectors: displacement, velocity, momentum **2** 9.22 N at 41° to the 7 N force **3** 240 m **4** 300 m **5** 1.25 m

P5d

1 50000 kg m/s **2** 16666.7 N **3** Momentum changes over longer period so less force on bones and muscles **4** 0.67 m/s to the right **5** 2 m/s opposite to the direction of the bullet

P5e & P5f

1 Their higher frequencies pass through the ionosphere without reflection; they are only diffracted by small amounts **2** Diagrams similar to those on page 53, top right **3** Diagrams similar to those on page 53, bottom right **4** If the path difference between the two waves is an equal number of half wavelengths, constructive interference occurs; if it is an odd number, destructive interference occurs **5** Particles would act as digital information – either there (on) or not there (off). Light waves would be subject to interference and diffraction producing hazy edges

P5g

1 A direction 90° to a line or surface **2** 200 000 000 m/s **3** It can only occur when light passes from a denser medium to one that is less dense **4** 1.32 **5** The incident ray of light has changed direction when it emerges from the prism. Each of the colours in the ray of white light travels a different distance within the prism and they are dispersed at different angles as they leave the prism. A ray of light travelling through a glass block has the incident and emergent rays parallel. All the colours in the ray have travelled exactly the same distance when they emerge from the block

P5h

1 The thicker the lens, the shorter the focal length **2** Diagram as on page 58, right-hand side; 14 cm **3** At 2f (f is the focal length) **4** 7.5 cm **5** So that a sharply focused image can form

P6a & P6b

1 2000 Ω **2** 48 V **3** An ohmic conductor has a resistance that remains constant so

long as its temperature remains constant; a non-ohmic conductor changes its resistance when either the voltage across it or the current through it changes **4** 8 V **5** The voltage across each resistor would be the same = 6 V

P6c

1 Diagram as shown on page 61, on left-hand side **2** No change **3** At a right angle **4** Zero force **5** Increased current, strength of magnetic field and number of turns in coil

P6d

1 When a wire cuts through magnetic field lines, a voltage is induced across the ends of the wire **2** Wire moved in opposite direction, direction of magnetic field reversed **3** Increase speed of movement of wire, increase strength of magnetic field **4** To conduct the current generated in the coil to the external circuit **5** (a) Diagram as on page 63, top right (b) Similar diagram as (a) but with two complete waves and twice the amplitude

P6e

1 Diagram as shown on page 64 **2** To prevent current from travelling into the transformer core instead of in wires around the coil **3** 12 V **4** Direct current produces a steady magnetic field instead of the changing field needed for electromagnetic induction **5** (a) 12 V (b) 0.5 A

P6f

1 Diagram of arrow with flat line against head of arrow (see similar symbols on page 66). Smaller arrow beneath with head pointing in the same direction as arrow above and labelled 'Direction of current' **2** Diagram as on page 66, left-hand column **3** Diagram as on page 66, bottom of left-hand column **4** The electrical insulation between the conducting plates prevents current from flowing **5** Diagram as on page 67, bottom left diagram, right-centre sketch of wave form with labelled axes added, vertical with 'Voltage' and horizontal with 'Time'

P6g & P6h

1 Diagram and truth table as shown on page 68 **2** The table should contain the following rows, under four columns labelled Input A, Input B, Input C and Output, respectively: 0,0,0,0; 1,0,0,0; 0,1,0,0; 0,0,1,1; 1,1,0,1; 0,1,1,1; 1,0,1,1; 1,1,1,1 **3** NOR gate **4** Relays can be used to control large currents in a circuit but they themselves can be controlled by small voltage logic gates. The relay isolates the logic gates from the mains **5** (a) The table should contain the following rows, under three columns labelled Input A, Input B, and Output, respectively: 0,0,0; 1,0,1; 0,1,1; 1,1,1 (b) An OR gate with output attached to an alarm and either input attached to a switch and 5 V DC supply